Southamerican
Cichlids II

Ulrich Glaser sen.
Wolfgang Glaser

Verlag: A.C.S. GmbH, Germany

Vorwort
Foreword

Das ist nun nach „LORICARIIDAE all L-NUMBERS" und „SOUTHAMERICAN CICHLIDS I" unser drittes Buch. Die guten Kritiken aus dem In- und Ausland beflügeln unsere Arbeit.

Dieser Bildband beinhaltet alle „Zwerge", so daß Sie dann mit Band I und dem in Kürze erscheinenden Band III, in dem auch die mittelamerikanischen vorgestellt werden, bereits fast ein komplettes Nachschlagewerk über alle südamerikanischen Buntbarsche besitzen.

Weitere Referenz-Hefte sind bereits in der Planung und es bleibt weiterhin unser Ziel alle Zierfische aus allen Erdteilen zu katalogisieren und daraus übersichtliche Bildbände zu erstellen, die es jedem Aquarianer, aber auch Händlern und Importeuren, auf einfachste Weise ermöglichen, *jeden* Fisch schnell und problemlos zu identifizieren und anhand des kurzen Symboltextes die wichtigsten Pflegegrundsätze zu erkennen.
Unsere Bücher enthalten in übersichtlicher Reihenfolge jeden bis jetzt bekannten Zierfisch nach einem genauen Code-Nummern-System geordnet, wobei jede Art ihre Code-Nummer hat und immer behält, selbst dann, wenn sich der Artname eventuell einmal ändern sollte.

Darüberhinaus wird jeder neu entdeckte oder neu gezüchtete Fisch jährlich in Bild und Kurztext als Ergänzung erscheinen, zusammen mit Infos über Namens-Änderungen etc., womit Sie mit unserem Werk dann immer "up to date" sind.

Dank unseres ausgeklügelten 7-stelligen Code-Nummern-Systems hat in Zukunft jeder Zierfisch an jedem Ort der Welt seine eigene Code-Nummer für immer, so daß sich unsere Bücher auch hervorragend und international als Katalog und Preisliste für den Handel eignen.

Unser Werk soll keinesfalls allgemein- oder artbezogene Fachliteratur überflüssig machen, sondern wir wollen Ihnen nur die unvorstellbare Arten-Vielfalt übersichtlich präsentieren und Ihnen die Möglichkeit geben, schnell und problemlos Ihre Fische zu bestimmen, für Pflege, Zucht etc. nehmen Sie sich bitte gute Fachbücher zur Hand, von denen es genügend gibt. Wir wünschen Ihnen viel Freude mit diesem Aqualog-Buch, Kritik immer willkommen, wir werden Ihre Anregungen in der Neuauflage berücksichtigen.

After the well-received volumes „LORICARIIDAE, all L-Numbers" and „SOUTH-AMERICAN CICHLIDS I" this is our third output. Positive reactions both home and abroad inspire our future work.

This volume contends all „dwarfs"; together with volume I and soon to be expected vol. III (containing also the Central-American species) you will have an almost complete encyclopedia of cichlids on your hands.

Further reference magazines are planned. We intend to catalogue all known ornamental fish and publish comprehensive books which make it possible, not only for every hobbyist, but also for professionals like traders and importers to easily define their fish.

Clearly arranged, our books contain every known ornamental fish, listed according to a precise code-number system in which each species is allotted a code-number, which remains the same, even if the name of the species changes.

Furthermore, each year a supplement will be published containing a picture and basic information on newly discovered or newly bred fish including information on name changes etc.
This means you will always be up to date with our reference work.

In the future, thanks to our ingenious 7-figure coding system, every ornamental fish in every part of the globe will have its own permanent code-number making our books eminently suitable as the basis for international catalogues and price-lists for the trade. This reference work is in no way intended to make other general or specific ornamental fish reference works redundant.
Instead our intention is to present the unbelievable variety of species in the clear format, enabling you to identify your fish quickly and simply. For information about care and breeding please consult any of the good specialist guide books, of which plenty are available.

We hope you enjoy using this Aqualog-Book. We are always pleased to receive your comments and criticism; this will then be taken into consideration in the new edition.

Mörfelden-Walldorf, März 1996

Ulrich Glaser sen.
Wolfgang Glaser

South American Cichlids II

Was sind Cichliden???

Cichliden und ihre nahen Verwandten leben auf drei Kontinenten, die meisten und gleichzeitig die farbenfreudigsten, in Afrika, Süd- und Mittelamerika.

In den deutschsprachigen Ländern werden Cichliden als "Buntbarsche" bezeichnet. Die meisten Europäer denken bei dem Wort "Barsch" an einen großen grauen Speisefisch. Dabei vergessen sie aber oft, daß es auch in Europa farbenfreudige Fische gibt, wie den Flußbarsch (Perca fluviatilis) oder den Sonnenbarsch (Lepomis gibbosus), der übrigens ursprünglich aus Nordamerika stammt. Diese beiden sind aber, wenngleich bunt, keine sonderlich nahen Verwandten der Cichliden. Die Cichliden - lediglich eine Familie in der riesigen Ordnung der Percoidea (barschartige Fische) - sind näher mit den im Meer lebenden Lippfischen verwandt. Nichtsdestoweniger sind aber größere Cichlidenarten in ihrer Heimat verbreitete Speisefische.

Innerhalb der Familie der Cichliden gibt es eine unvorstellbare Formenfülle. Manche sind winzige Zwerge, die kaum länger als 3 oder 4 cm werden, andere sind 100 cm lange Riesen. Sie können langgestreckt sein, wie die Hecht-Cichliden oder hochrückig; manche sind von typischer Fisch-Gestalt, andere geradezu bizarr geformt; wir kennen scheibenförmige, wie den Discus und "Bullen", wie manche Cichlasoma.

Cichliden sind Individualisten. Das gilt sowohl für die Einzeltiere wie auch für die einzelnen Arten. Keiner gleicht vollständig dem anderen. Die meisten, wenn auch nicht alle, zeigen einen ausgeprägten Reviersinn. So gibt es zwar auch "friedliche", die sich harmonisch in ein Gesellschaftsaquarium einfügen. Andere aber sind mehr oder weniger "aggressiv". Und es gibt auch ausgesprochene "Schlägertypen", die permanent auf Händel, auch mit Artangehörigen, aus sind.

Alle diese Aussagen sind auch auf Südamerikanische Cichliden zutreffend. So sollte die Auswahl von Fischen, die später ein gemeinsames Aquarium bewohnen sollen, sehr sorgfältig erfolgen.

In unserem Buch "Südamerikanische Cichliden I" stellten wir alle bislang importierten Cichla, Crenicichla, Geophagus etc. vor. Die meisten von ihnen sind großwüchsige Fische. Dementsprechend benötigen sie auch große Aquarien.

In diesem Band präsentieren wir südamerikanische Zwergcichliden. Keiner von ihnen wird größer als 10 cm. Die Aquarien für diese Fische können also auch etwas kleiner sein. Der Pfleger hat aber zu beachten, daß die meisten dieser Zwerge weiches und saures Wasser benötigen, um sich wohlzufühlen und ihr interessantes Verhalten zu zeigen. Die meisten fressen jedes gängige Fischfutter, viele bevorzugen jedoch lebendes oder Frost-Futter.

Eine große Zahl dieser Zwerge ist leuchtend gefärbt, jede Art fasziniert den Pfleger mit ihrem Balz- und Brutpflege-Verhalten.

Obwohl es sich um kleine Fische handelt, sollte das Aquarium dennoch nicht zu klein sein. Üblicherweise pflegt man ein Männchen mit drei oder vier Weibchen, denn es handelt sich um sog. agame Fische. Jeder Fisch, egal ob männlichen oder weiblichen Geschlechts, bezieht sein eigenes kleines Revier, das etwa 10-15 qcm Fläche umfaßt. Die einzige bekannte Ausnahme ist der Apistogramma spec. "Smaragd". Bei dieser Art verpaart sich ein Weibchen mit drei bis vier Männchen. Und in der Gattung Crenicara (nicht bei den Dicrossus!) ist grundsätzlich jedes Tier ein Weibchen, mit Ausnahme des ranghöchsten Tieres. Sogar ein Weibchen, das bereits Eier gelegt hat, kann sich (aus einer Gruppe von Weibchen heraus) zu einem funktionstüchtigen Männchen verwandeln, wenn das Männchen stirbt oder entfernt wird. Es ist leicht einzusehen, daß zwei Gruppen von 1,3 (d.h. 1 Männchen und drei Weibchen) Zwergcichliden ein Aquarium von ca. 100 cm Länge benötigen. Darüber hinaus: Aquarien solcher Größe sind weitaus leichter zu pflegen als kleinere.

Damit die Fische sich wohlfühlen, sollten Pflanzen, Steine und Wurzeln im Aquarium vorhanden sein. Diese optischen Marken werden zu zentralen Punkten bei der Revierbildung der Fische. In solchen Aquarien zeigen Zwergcichliden ihr faszinierendes natürliches Verhalten. Bei der Auswahl der Steine muß der Pfleger darauf achten, daß die Steine nicht kalkhaltig sind, denn kalkhaltiges Wasser bekommt den Südamerikanischen Zwergcichliden garnicht.

Der größte Teil der in den Zoofachgeschäften der Welt angebotenen Zwergcichliden besteht bereits aus Nachzucht-Exemplaren und von manchen, speziell von Apistogramma cacatuoides und A. borellii existieren herrliche Zuchtformen.

Die Gattung Apistogramma ist für die Wissenschaft hochkompliziert, denn diese Fische zeigen eine ungeheure Variabilität. Gerade Aquarianer, die sich mit Importen befassen, können mit der Veröffentlichung ihrer Beobachtungen der Wissenschaft helfen, diese problematische Gattung zu verstehen.

Wundervoll gefärbte Cichliden leben nicht nur in Südamerika. Viele von ihnen stammen aus Mittel-Amerika. Sie werden Ihnen bald vorgestellt werden - in SOUTHAMERICAN CICHLIDS III:

Detaillierte Fundortangaben sind mit Vorsicht zu genießen. In vielen Regionen (z.B. im Pantanal) werden weitflächige Gebiete bei jeder Regenzeit überflutet und dabei bekommen unterschiedliche Flußsysteme Kontakt zueinander. Das ist durchaus vergleichbar mit einem Fisch, der in Frankreich beschrieben wurde und dann plötzlich in Russland auftauchte.

Diese Sumpfgebiete sind unglaublich große Wasserflächen. Sie beinhalten eine unbeschreibliche Anzahl von Fischen - so lange der Lebensraum intakt bleibt. Eine Frage, die uns alle angeht. Süßwassergebiete in den Tropen können nicht überfischt werden. Das Verhalten der in diesen Gebieten lebenden Fische macht das unmöglich. Lediglich die Vergiftung und Zerstörung der Biotope gefährdet alle hier lebenden Tier- und Pflanzenarten.

Der Zierfisch-Fang ist für viele Menschen in diesen Gebieten die einzige Einkommensquelle. Nebenbei werden diese, an sich "unnützen" Fische, plötzlich wertvoll für die Menschen dieser Regionen. Ohne den Zierfischhandel würde sich kein Mensch darum scheren, ob da eine Art mehr oder weniger existiert.

Die meisten Südamerikanischen Cichliden passen sich dem Leben im Aquarium leicht an. In ihrem natürlichen Lebensraum müssen sie sich ja auch mit den wechselnden Bedingungen zu jeder Jahreszeit arrangieren.

Die Symbole, die wir angeben, beschreiben die wesentlichsten Aquarien-Bedingungen. Wenn Sie Ihren Fischen optimale Bedingungen schaffen, werden Sie mit einer wundervollen Farbenpracht und einer hohen Lebhaftigkeit Ihrer Fische belohnt werden. Und für einen echten Aquarianer ist nichts mit dem Gefühl zu vergleichen, wie dem, das man beim Anblick einer gerade freischwimmenden neuen Generation Cichliden in seinem Aquarium empfindet.

© A.C.S. Glaser GmbH

South American Cichlids II

What are Cichlids???

Cichlids and their close relatives are found on three continents, most of them (the most colourful, too) in Africa, South- and Central-America.

The german word for Cichlids is "Buntbarsche", which means Ornamental Perches. Most Europeans picture a perch as a large, grey, edible fish. They forget that even in Europe there are colourful fish like the Common Perch (Perca fluviatilis) or the Pumpkin-Seed Perch (Lepomis gibbosus), the latter originating in North-America. Both are , although colourful, not closley related to the Cichlids. Cichlids, being one familiy in the giantic order of the Percoidea (the perch-like fish) are closer related to the marine lippfish. Nevertheless, the larger species among them often make a delicious dish in their native countries.

There is an incredible large number of different types within the cichlid family. Some of them are small fry, not growing bigger than 3 or 4 cm in length and giants reaching over 100 cm. They may be elongated (as the pike-cichlids) or high bodied; some show typical "fish" shape, some look quite bizarre; we also know plate-shaped ones, like the discus and bulls, of the "Cichlasoma"- genus.

Cichlids are individualists, in referd of the species and as well as individuals. Not one of them is absolutely similar to another. They are usually, though not exclusively, territorial by nature. There are entirely "peaceful" ones which are perfectly suited for a mixed aquarium. Others are "aggressive" to a greater or lesser extent. There are even "belligerent" ones, looking for fights even among their own kind.

The points made above are especially true for the South-American cichlids, so one should be extra-careful when choosing the species to be put together in a tank.

In our book "South-American Cichlids I" we introduced to you all the Cichla, Crenicichla, Geophagus etc.. Most of them are large-growing fish that obviuesy need appropriate tanks.

In this book we present the South-American dwarf-cichlids. None of them grows bigger than 10 cm. Aquaria for those fish may be of a smaller size. The keeper has to keep in mind that most of these dwarfs need soft water with an acidic reaction to feel well and show the behaviour that makes them so interesting to watch. Most of them eat the usual fish food, but they prefer living and frozen food.

A large number of the dwarfs is brightly coloured, every single one of them fascinates the keeper with its mating and breeding behaviour.

Although they are small fish, the aquarium should not be too small. Usually one has to keep one male with three or four females, because they are so-called "agam" fish. Each fish, both male and female will build up its own small territorium of about 10-15 cm2. The only exception known is the Apistogramma spec. "smaragd". This species finds one female mating with three or four males. In the genus Crenicara (not Dicrossus!) every individual is a female, exept for the highest in range. Even a female (out of a group of females) that has bred before may change into a functional male, when the original male dies or is taken away. It is rather dear that two groups of 1,3 (which means 1 male and three females) dwarf-cichlids need an aquarium of about 100 cm length. By the way: aquaria of this size are much easier to tend than smaller ones.

To make the fish feel comfortable, there should be plants, stones and roots in the aquarium. These optical marks will become the center of the individual territoria. In such aquaria the dwarf cichlids will certainly show their fascinating natural behaviour.The choosen stones should not be stones chalky, for hard water harmes the South-American dwarf-cichlids.

The most of the South-American dwarf-cichlids that are found in the petshops around the world are born in captivity and of some of them, especially Apistogramma cactuoides and A. borellii, developed wonderful breeds.

The genus Apistogramma is one of the most complicated for scientists, for these fish show an unbelievable number of variations. Therefore aquarists who are dealing with imported forms can help the ichtyologists with the publication of their observations in understanding this problematic genus.

Wonderfully coloured cichlids do not live exclusively in South-America -there are also numerous species originating from also origin from Central-America. They are coming to you soon in SOUTHAMERICAN CICHLIDS III..

Details of a fish´s place of origin should be regarded with caution. In many regions (e.g. Pantanal) vast areas are flooded every rainy season and whole river systems become connected with each other. The outcome is comparable to a fish from France that is found in Russia.

In the resueting marshland with its large streches of water an incredible variety of fish exist - as long as these biotopes remain intact. All of us should support the preservation of these marshes.Freshwater areas in the tropics cannot be overfished. The behaviour of the fish makes shure that this will never happen. Only the poisoning and destroying of the biotopes endangers all the animals and plants living there.

In those regions the catching of ornamental fish is for many people the sole source of income. In this regard only living fish are of interest for the people in the native countries. Otherwise no one would take care for the existence of one species more or less.

Most South-American cichlids adapt easily to the conditions in the aquarium. In their natural environment they have to accommodate to changing water conditions with each new season.

The figures we give refer to the common aquarium values. In case you provide your fish with optimum conditions you will be rewarded with a wonderful display of colours and a high level of vitality. For an aquarium enthusiast, there is nothing that beats the feeling when the next generation of successfully-bred cichlids starts swimming.

Inhalt / Contents :

Bestimmungsmerkmale von Apistogramma- Arten

Determination-signs for Apistogramma-species

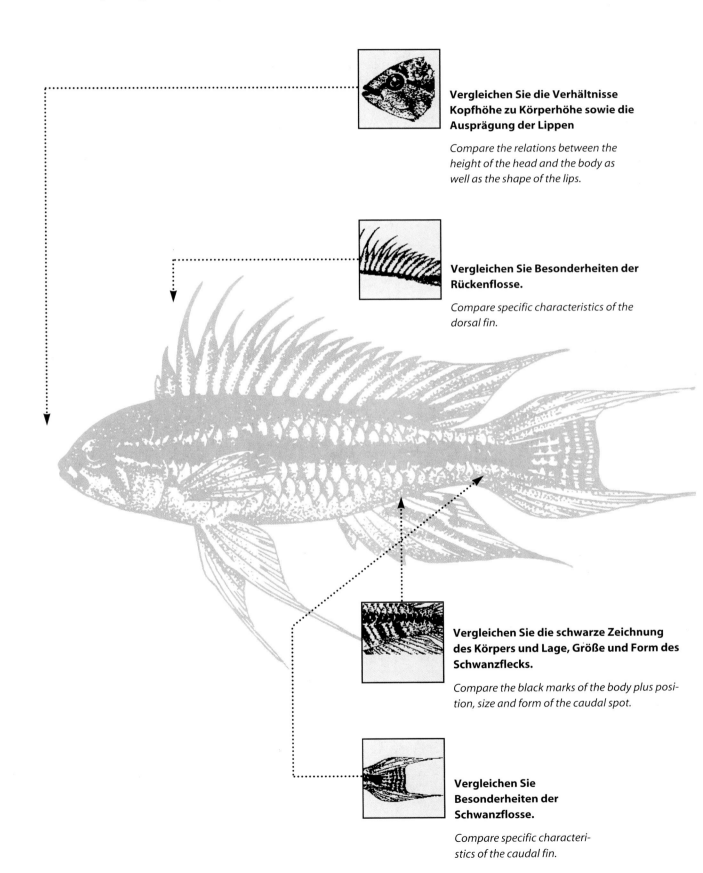

Vergleichen Sie die Verhältnisse Kopfhöhe zu Körperhöhe sowie die Ausprägung der Lippen

Compare the relations between the height of the head and the body as well as the shape of the lips.

Vergleichen Sie Besonderheiten der Rückenflosse.

Compare specific characteristics of the dorsal fin.

Vergleichen Sie die schwarze Zeichnung des Körpers und Lage, Größe und Form des Schwanzflecks.

Compare the black marks of the body plus position, size and form of the caudal spot.

Vergleichen Sie Besonderheiten der Schwanzflosse.

Compare specific characteristics of the caudal fin.

Apistogramma + Microgeophagus

nach geografischen Gesichtspunkten

in geographical order

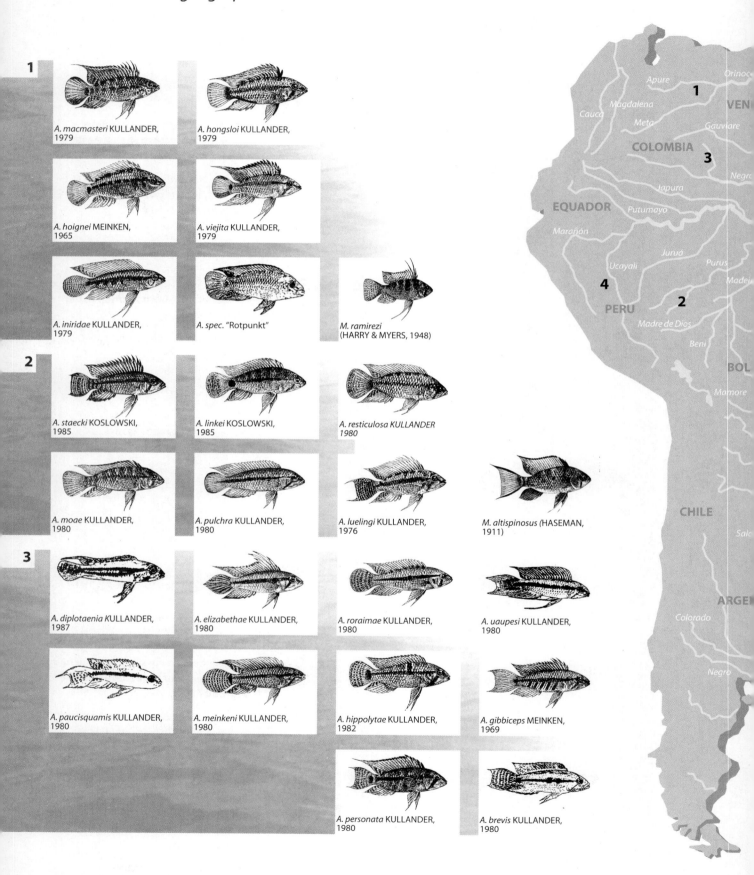

1

A. macmasteri KULLANDER, 1979

A. hongsloi KULLANDER, 1979

A. hoignei MEINKEN, 1965

A. viejita KULLANDER, 1979

A. iniridae KULLANDER, 1979

A. spec. "Rotpunkt"

M. ramirezi (HARRY & MYERS, 1948)

2

A. staecki KOSLOWSKI, 1985

A. linkei KOSLOWSKI, 1985

A. resticulosa KULLANDER 1980

A. moae KULLANDER, 1980

A. pulchra KULLANDER, 1980

A. luelingi KULLANDER, 1976

M. altispinosus (HASEMAN, 1911)

3

A. diplotaenia KULLANDER, 1987

A. elizabethae KULLANDER, 1980

A. roraimae KULLANDER, 1980

A. uaupesi KULLANDER, 1980

A. paucisquamis KULLANDER, 1980

A. meinkeni KULLANDER, 1980

A. hippolytae KULLANDER, 1982

A. gibbiceps MEINKEN, 1969

A. personata KULLANDER, 1980

A. brevis KULLANDER, 1980

© **A.C.S. Glaser GmbH**

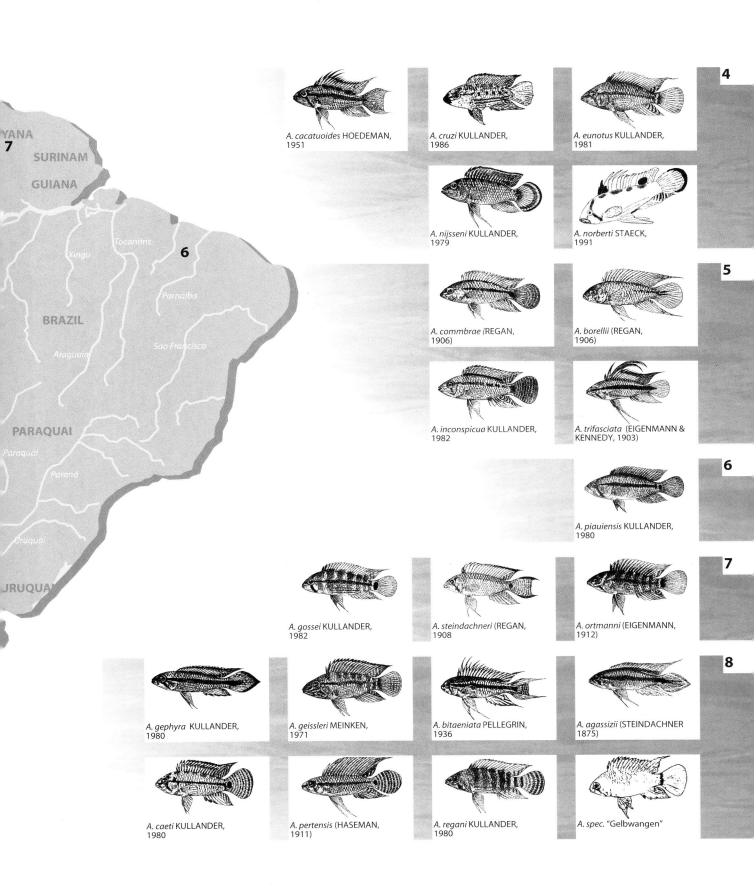

YANA

SURINAM

GUIANA

7

Tocantins

Xingu

6

Parnaiba

BRAZIL

Araguaia

Sao Francisco

PARAQUAI

Paraquai

Parană

Paraná

Uruquai

URUQUAI

4

A. cacatuoides HOEDEMAN,
1951

A. cruzi KULLANDER,
1986

A. eunotus KULLANDER,
1981

A. nijsseni KULLANDER,
1979

A. norberti STAECK,
1991

5

A. commbrae (REGAN,
1906)

A. borellii (REGAN,
1906)

A. inconspicua KULLANDER,
1982

A. trifasciata (EIGENMANN &
KENNEDY, 1903)

6

A. piauiensis KULLANDER,
1980

7

A. gossei KULLANDER,
1982

A. steindachneri (REGAN,
1908)

A. ortmanni (EIGENMANN,
1912)

8

A. gephyra KULLANDER,
1980

A. geissleri MEINKEN,
1971

A. bitaeniata PELLEGRIN,
1936

A. agassizii (STEINDACHNER
1875)

A. caeti KULLANDER,
1980

A. pertensis (HASEMAN,
1911)

A. regani KULLANDER,
1980

A. spec. "Gelbwangen"

Apistogramma
Bestimmungstabelle
Determination-chart

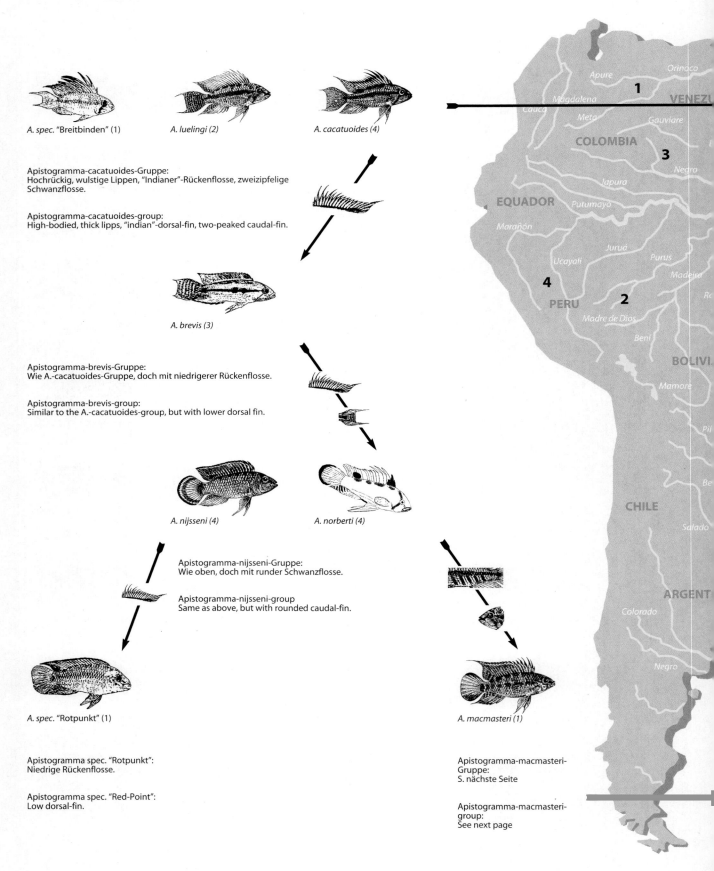

A. spec. "Breitbinden" (1)

A. luelingi (2)

A. cacatuoides (4)

Apistogramma-cacatuoides-Gruppe:
Hochrückig, wulstige Lippen, "Indianer"-Rückenflosse, zweizipfelige Schwanzflosse.

Apistogramma-cacatuoides-group:
High-bodied, thick lipps, "indian"-dorsal-fin, two-peaked caudal-fin.

A. brevis (3)

Apistogramma-brevis-Gruppe:
Wie A.-cacatuoides-Gruppe, doch mit niedrigerer Rückenflosse.

Apistogramma-brevis-group:
Similar to the A.-cacatuoides-group, but with lower dorsal fin.

A. nijsseni (4)

A. norberti (4)

Apistogramma-nijsseni-Gruppe:
Wie oben, doch mit runder Schwanzflosse.

Apistogramma-nijsseni-group
Same as above, but with rounded caudal-fin.

A. spec. "Rotpunkt" (1)

A. macmasteri (1)

Apistogramma spec. "Rotpunkt":
Niedrige Rückenflosse.

Apistogramma spec. "Red-Point":
Low dorsal-fin.

Apistogramma-macmasteri-Gruppe:
S. nächste Seite

Apistogramma-macmasteri-group:
See next page

© A.C.S. Glaser GmbH

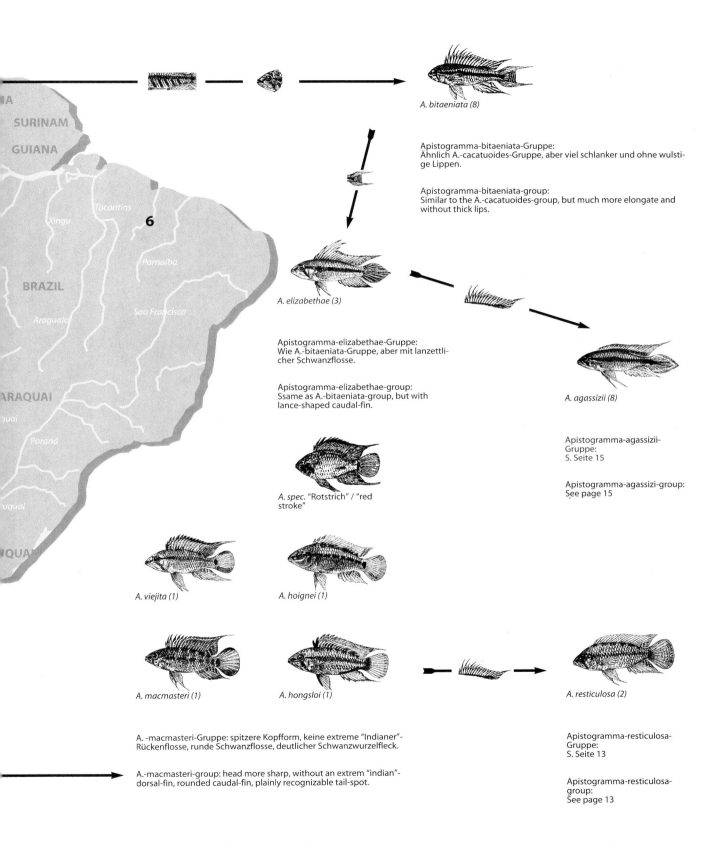

A. bitaeniata (8)

Apistogramma-bitaeniata-Gruppe:
Ähnlich A.-cacatuoides-Gruppe, aber viel schlanker und ohne wulstige Lippen.

Apistogramma-bitaeniata-group:
Similar to the A.-cacatuoides-group, but much more elongate and without thick lips.

A. elizabethae (3)

A. agassizii (8)

Apistogramma-elizabethae-Gruppe:
Wie A.-bitaeniata-Gruppe, aber mit lanzettlicher Schwanzflosse.

Apistogramma-elizabethae-group:
Ssame as A.-bitaeniata-group, but with lance-shaped caudal-fin.

Apistogramma-agassizii-
Gruppe:
S. Seite 15

Apistogramma-agassizi-group:
See page 15

A. spec. "Rotstrich" / "red stroke"

A. viejita (1)

A. hoignei (1)

A. macmasteri (1)

A. hongsloi (1)

A. resticulosa (2)

Apistogramma-resticulosa-
Gruppe:
S. Seite 13

Apistogramma-resticulosa-
group:
See page 13

A. -macmasteri-Gruppe: spitzere Kopfform, keine extreme "Indianer"-Rückenflosse, runde Schwanzflosse, deutlicher Schwanzwurzelfleck.

A.-macmasteri-group: head more sharp, without an extrem "indian"-dorsal-fin, rounded caudal-fin, plainly recognizable tail-spot.

Apistogramma
Bestimmungstabelle
Determination-chart

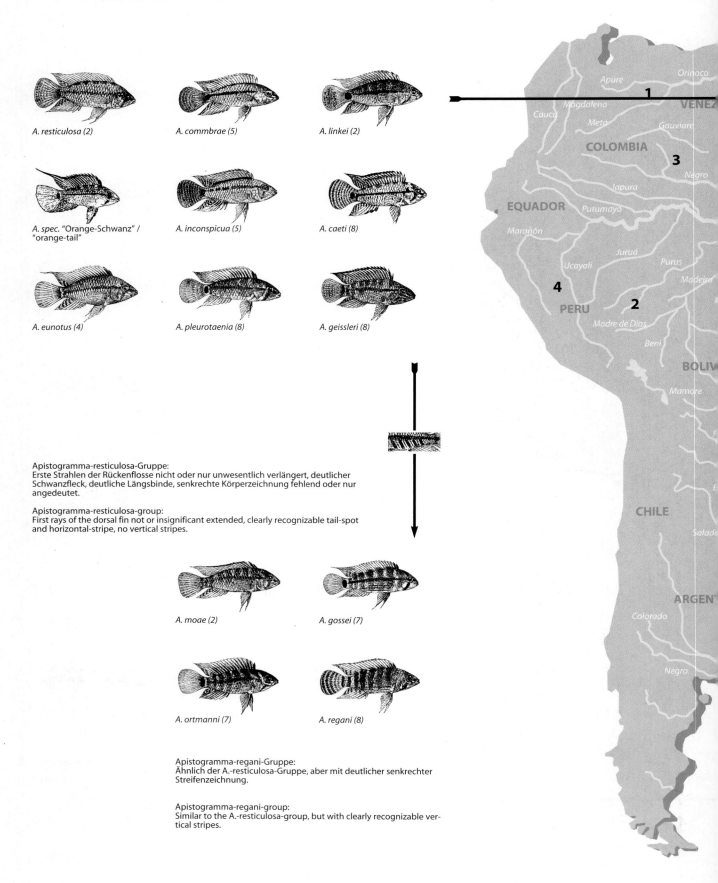

A. resticulosa (2)

A. commbrae (5)

A. linkei (2)

A. spec. "Orange-Schwanz" / "orange-tail"

A. inconspicua (5)

A. caeti (8)

A. eunotus (4)

A. pleurotaenia (8)

A. geissleri (8)

Apistogramma-resticulosa-Gruppe:
Erste Strahlen der Rückenflosse nicht oder nur unwesentlich verlängert, deutlicher Schwanzfleck, deutliche Längsbinde, senkrechte Körperzeichnung fehlend oder nur angedeutet.

Apistogramma-resticulosa-group:
First rays of the dorsal fin not or insignificant extended, clearly recognizable tail-spot and horizontal-stripe, no vertical stripes.

A. moae (2)

A. gossei (7)

A. ortmanni (7)

A. regani (8)

Apistogramma-regani-Gruppe:
Ähnlich der A.-resticulosa-Gruppe, aber mit deutlicher senkrechter Streifenzeichnung.

Apistogramma-regani-group:
Similar to the A.-resticulosa-group, but with clearly recognizable vertical stripes.

© A.C.S. Glaser GmbH

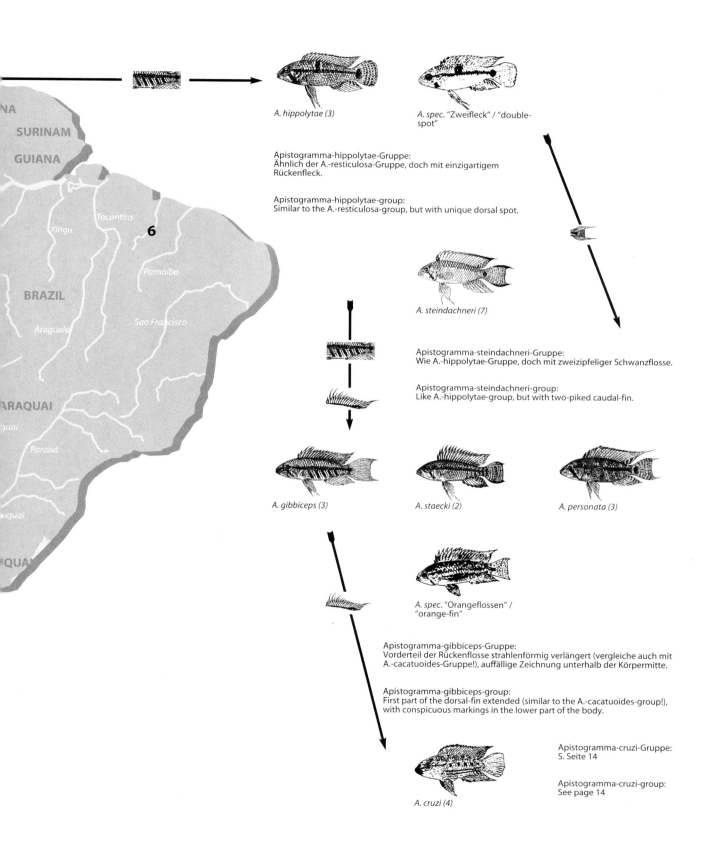

A. hippolytae (3)

A. spec. "Zweifleck" / "double-spot"

Apistogramma-hippolytae-Gruppe:
Ähnlich der A.-resticulosa-Gruppe, doch mit einzigartigem Rückenfleck.

Apistogramma-hippolytae-group:
Similar to the A.-resticulosa-group, but with unique dorsal spot.

A. steindachneri (7)

Apistogramma-steindachneri-Gruppe:
Wie A.-hippolytae-Gruppe, doch mit zweizipfeliger Schwanzflosse.

Apistogramma-steindachneri-group:
Like A.-hippolytae-group, but with two-piked caudal-fin.

A. gibbiceps (3)

A. staecki (2)

A. personata (3)

A. spec. "Orangeflossen" / "orange-fin"

Apistogramma-gibbiceps-Gruppe:
Vorderteil der Rückenflosse strahlenförmig verlängert (vergleiche auch mit A.-cacatuoides-Gruppe!), auffällige Zeichnung unterhalb der Körpermitte.

Apistogramma-gibbiceps-group:
First part of the dorsal-fin extended (similar to the A.-cacatuoides-group!), with conspicuous markings in the lower part of the body.

Apistogramma-cruzi-Gruppe:
S. Seite 14

Apistogramma-cruzi-group:
See page 14

A. cruzi (4)

Apistogramma
Bestimmungstabelle
Determination-chart

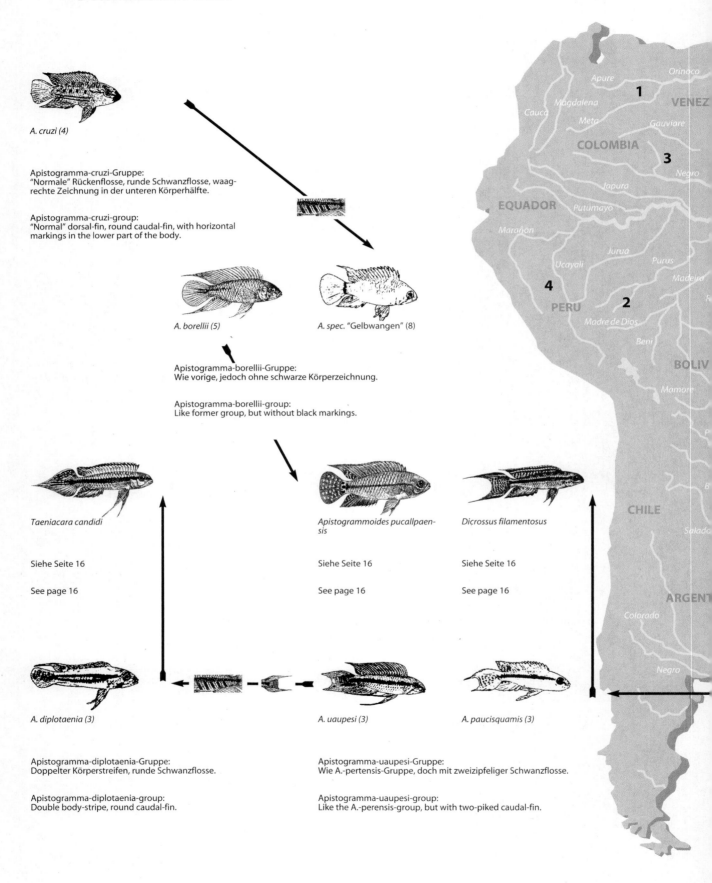

A. cruzi (4)

Apistogramma-cruzi-Gruppe:
"Normale" Rückenflosse, runde Schwanzflosse, waag-
rechte Zeichnung in der unteren Körperhälfte.

Apistogramma-cruzi-group:
"Normal" dorsal-fin, round caudal-fin, with horizontal
markings in the lower part of the body.

A. borellii (5)

A. spec. "Gelbwangen" (8)

Apistogramma-borellii-Gruppe:
Wie vorige, jedoch ohne schwarze Körperzeichnung.

Apistogramma-borellii-group:
Like former group, but without black markings.

Taeniacara candidi

Apistogrammoides pucallpaensis

Dicrossus filamentosus

Siehe Seite 16

Siehe Seite 16

Siehe Seite 16

See page 16

See page 16

See page 16

A. diplotaenia (3)

A. uaupesi (3)

A. paucisquamis (3)

Apistogramma-diplotaenia-Gruppe:
Doppelter Körperstreifen, runde Schwanzflosse.

Apistogramma-uaupesi-Gruppe:
Wie A.-pertensis-Gruppe, doch mit zweizipfeliger Schwanzflosse.

Apistogramma-diplotaenia-group:
Double body-stripe, round caudal-fin.

Apistogramma-uaupesi-group:
Like the A.-perensis-group, but with two-piked caudal-fin.

© **A.C.S. Glaser GmbH**

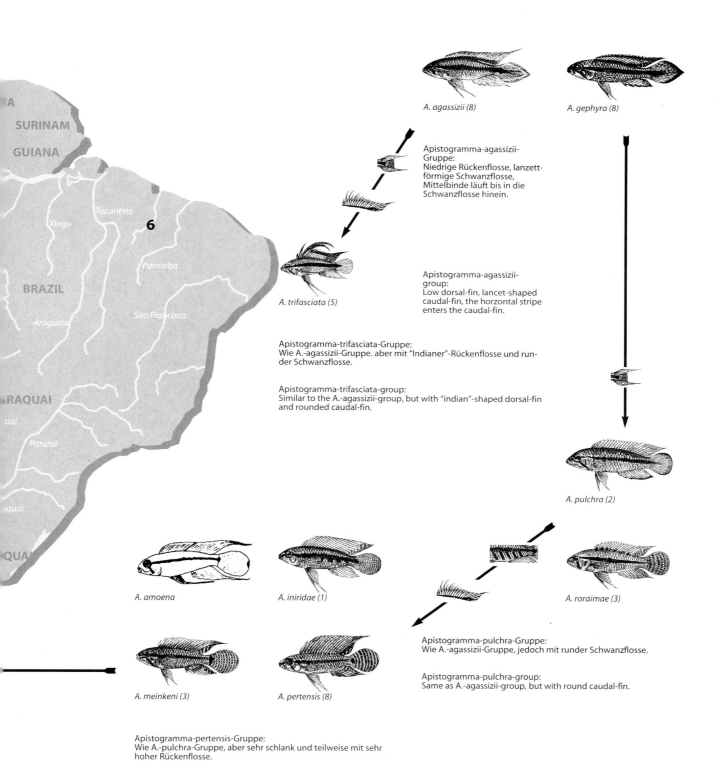

A. agassizii (8)

A. gephyra (8)

Apistogramma-agassizii-Gruppe:
Niedrige Rückenflosse, lanzett-förmige Schwanzflosse, Mittelbinde läuft bis in die Schwanzflosse hinein.

Apistogramma-agassizii-group:
Low dorsal-fin, lancet-shaped caudal-fin, the horzontal stripe enters the caudal-fin.

A. trifasciata (5)

Apistogramma-trifasciata-Gruppe:
Wie A.-agassizii-Gruppe. aber mit "Indianer"-Rückenflosse und runder Schwanzflosse.

Apistogramma-trifasciata-group:
Similar to the A.-agassizii-group, but with "indian"-shaped dorsal-fin and rounded caudal-fin.

A. pulchra (2)

A. amoena

A. iniridae (1)

A. roraimae (3)

A. meinkeni (3)

A. pertensis (8)

Apistogramma-pulchra-Gruppe:
Wie A.-agassizii-Gruppe, jedoch mit runder Schwanzflosse.

Apistogramma-pulchra-group:
Same as A.-agassizii-group, but with round caudal-fin.

Apistogramma-pertensis-Gruppe:
Wie A.-pulchra-Gruppe, aber sehr schlank und teilweise mit sehr hoher Rückenflosse.

Apistogramma-pertensis-group:
Similar to the A.-pulchra-group, but body very slim, particulary with very high dorsal-fin.

Geographische Verbreitung der übrigen Zwergcichliden
geographical distribution of the other dwarf-cichlids

3

Taeniacara candidi

4

Apistogrammoides pucallpaen-sis

3

Dicrossus filamentosus

7

Nannacara aureocephala

7

Nannacara anomala

8

Biotoecus opercularis

8

Crenicara punctulata

© A.C.S. Glaser GmbH

S03305-3 Apistogramma agassizii MALE
AGASSIZII - DWARF-CICHLID
Amazonas-AREA, Brazil, W, 8-9 cm

S03305-3 Apistogramma agassizii FEMALE
AGASSIZII - DWARF-CICHLID
Amazonas-AREA, Brazil, W, 8-9 cm

S03310-3 Apistogramma agassizii "BLUE"
BLUE-AGASSIZII - DWARF-CICHLID
Amazonas-AREA, Brazil, W, 8-9 cm

S03315-4 Apistogramma agassizii "DOUBLE-RED"
DOUBLE-RED - AGASSIZII MALE
Amazonas-AREA, Brazil, Z, 8-10 cm

S03315-4 Apistogramma agassizii "DOUBLE-RED"
DOUBLE-RED - AGASSIZII FEMALE with spawn
Amazonas-AREA, Brazil, Z, 8-10cm

S03320-4 Apistogramma agassizii "ORANGE-TAIL"
ORANGE-TAIL - AGASSIZII MALE
Amazonas-AREA, Brazil, Z, 8-10cm

S03320-4 Apistogramma agassizii "ORANGE-TAIL"
ORANGE-TAIL - AGASSIZII FEMALE with spawn
Amazonas-AREA, Brazil,, Z, 8-10cm

S03323-3 Apistogramma agassizii "IQUITOS"
IQUITOS - AGASSIZII
Amazonas-AREA, Brazil, W, 8-10cm

S03325-3 Apistogramma agassizii "RED"
RED - AGASSIZII
Amazonas-AREA, Brazil,, Z, 8-10cm

S03325-3 Apistogramma agassizii "RED"
RED - AGASSIZII
Amazonas-AREA, Brazil,, Z, 8-10cm

S03327-4 Apistogramma agassizii "RED-GOLD"
RED-GOLD - AGASSIZII MALE
Amazonas-AREA, Brazil,, Z, 8-10cm

S03327-4 Apistogramma agassizii "RED-GOLD"
RED-GOLD - AGASSIZII FEMALE
Amazonas-AREA, Brazil,, Z, 8-10cm

S03330-4 Apistogramma agassizii "REDTAIL"
REDTAIL - AGASSIZII MALE
Amazonas-AREA, Brazil,, Z, 8-10cm

S03330-4 Apistogramma agassizii "REDTAIL"
REDTAIL - AGASSIZII PAIR
Amazonas-AREA, Brazil,, Z, 8-10cm

S03332-4 Apistogramma agassizii "EAST-REDTAIL"
EAST - REDTAIL - AGASSIZII
Amazonas-AREA, Brazil,, Z, 8-10cm

S03334-4 Apistogramma agassizii "HÜSER-REDTAIL"
HÜSER - REDTAIL - AGASSIZII MALE
Amazonas-AREA, Brazil,, Z, 8-10cm

© **A.C.S. Glaser GmbH**

S03336-4 Apistogramma agassizii "SANTAREM"
SANTAREM - AGASSIZII
Amazonas-AREA, Brazil,, Z, 8-10cm

S03338-3 Apistogramma agassizii "WHITETAIL"
WHITETAIL - AGASSIZII MALE
Amazonas-AREA, Brazil, W, 8-10cm

S03340-3 Apistogramma cf. agassizii "TEFE"
TEFE - AGASSIZII MALE
Amazonas-AREA, BraziL; W, 8-10cm

S03342-3 Apistogramma agassizii "TEFE-REDTAIL"
TEFE-REDTAIL - AGASSIZII MALE
Amazonas-AREA, Brazil, W, 8-10cm

S03344-2   Apistogramma sp. aff. agassizii "BELEM"
BELEM - AGASSIZII
Amazonas-AREA, Brazil, W, 8-10cm

S03344-4   Apistogramma sp. aff. agassizii "BELEM"
BELEM - AGASSIZII
Amazonas-AREA, Brazil, W, 8-10cm

S03313-4 Apistogramma agassizii "BLUETAIL"
BLUETAIL - AGASSIZII MALE
Amazonas-AREA, Brazil, W, 8-10cm

S03313-4 Apistogramma agassizii "BLUETAIL"
BLUETAIL - AGASSIZII MALE
Amazonas-AREA, Brazil, W, 8-10cm

S03360-3 Apistogramma bitaeniata (= kleei) MALE
BITAENIATA - DWARF-CICHLID
Amazonas-Area Peru+Brazil, B, Male 6cm, Female 4cm
♂ ▷ ₽ ◑ ☺ ☺ 🎴 🖼 🐟 ◇ 🔟

S03360-3 Apistogramma bitaeniata (= kleei) FEMALE
BITAENIATA - DWARF-CICHLID
Amazonas-Area Peru+Brazil, B, Male 6cm, Female 4cm
♀ ▷ ₽ ◑ ☺ ☺ 🎴 🖼 🐟 ◇ 🔟

S03362-3 Apistogramma bitaeniata "BLUE" MALE
BLUE-BITAENIATA - DWARF-CICHLID
Amazonas-Area Peru+Brazil, B, Male 6cm, Female 4cm
♂ ▷ ₽ ◑ ☺ ☺ 🎴 🖼 🐟 ◇ 🔟

S03362-3 Apistogramma bitaeniata "BLUE" FEMALE
BLUE-BITAENIATA - DWARF-CICHLID
Amazonas-Area Peru+Brazil, B, Male 6cm, Female 4cm
♀ ▷ ₽ ◑ ☺ ☺ 🎴 🖼 🐟 ◇ 🔟

S03364-4 Apistogramma bitaeniata "BROWN-RED"
BROWNY - DWARF-CICHLID colour-variation
Amazonas-Area Peru+Brazil, B, Male 6cm, Female 4cm
▷ ₽ ◑ ☺ ☺ 🎴 🖼 🐟 ◇ 🔟

S03368-4 Apistogramma bitaeniata "LIGHT-BLUE" MALE
LIGHT-BLUE - DWARF-CICHLID colour-variation
Amazonas-Area Peru+Brazil, B, Male 6cm, Female 4cm
♂ ▷ ₽ ◑ ☺ ☺ 🎴 🖼 🐟 ◇ 🔟

Crenicichla sp. "XINGU III"
Der, und alle anderen in / all other you will find
in "SOUTHAMERICAN - CICHLIDS I"

Cichlasoma (Heros) festae blue
Der, und alle anderen in / all other you will find
in "SOUTHAMERICAN - CICHLIDS III"

© A.C.S. Glaser GmbH

S03366-3 Apistogramma bitaeniata "GREEN-SPOTTED"
GREEN-SPOTTED - DWARF-CICHLID MALE
Amazonas-Area Peru+Brazil, W, 4-6cm, colour-variation

S03366-3 Apistogramma bitaeniata "GREEN-SPOTTED"
GREEN-SPOTTED - DWARF-CICHLID FEMALE
Amazonas-Area Peru+Brazil, W, 4-6cm, colour-variation

S03370-3 Apistogramma bitaeniata "PERU-BLUE" MALE
PERU-BLUE - DWARF-CICHLID colour-variation
Peru, W, Male 6cm, Female 4cm

S03372-4 Apistogramma bitaeniata "RED" MALE
RED - BITAENIATA-DWAR colour-variation
Peru, B, Male 6cm, Female 4cm

S03372-4 Apistogramma bitaeniata "RED" PAIR
RED - BITAENIATA-DWAR colour-variation
Peru, B, Male 6cm, Female 4cm

S03376-4 Apistogramma bitaeniata (= kleei) MALE
KLEEI - DWARF-CICHLID
Peru, W, 5-7cm

S03376-4 Apistogramma bitaeniata (= kleei) FEMALE
KLEEI - DWARF-CICHLID
Peru, W, 5-7cm

S03378-4 Apistogramma bitaeniata "YELLOW" MALE
YELLOW-BITAENIATA - DWARF
Peru, B, 5-7cm

APISTOGRAMMA AGASSIZII "REDTAIL"

APISTOGRAMMA AGASSIZII "DOUBLE-RED"

© **A.C.S. Glaser GmbH**

APISTOGRAMMA BITAENIATA "BLUE" (= klausewitzi)

S03385-4 Apistogramma borellii "BLUE" MALE
BORELLI-BLUE - DWARF (before Ap. reitzigi)
Mato-Grosso - Area, W, Male 8cm, Female 5cm
♂ ▷ ♫ ◑ ☺ ☺ ⊞ 🖼 ➤ ◈ 🔲

S03385-4 Apistogramma borellii "BLUE" FEMALE
BORELLI-BLUE - DWARF (before Ap. reitzigi)
Mato-Grosso - Area, W, Male 8cm, Female 5cm
♀ ▷ ♫ ◑ ☺ ☺ ⊞ 🖼 ➤ ◈ 🔲

S03388-3 Apistogramma borellii "ROYAL-BLUE" MALE
BORELLI-ROYAL-BLUE - DWARF
Mato-Grosso - Area, W, Male 8cm, Female 5cm
♂ ▷ ♫ ◑ ☺ ☺ ⊞ 🖼 ➤ ◈ 🔲

S03383-4 Apistogramma borellii MALE
BORELLI - DWARF-CICHLID (before Ap. reitzigi)
Mato-Grosso - Area, B, Male 8cm, Female 5cm
♂ ▷ ♫ ◑ ☺ ☺ ⊞ 🖼 ➤ ◈ 🔲

S03383-4 Apistogramma borellii FEMALE
BORELLI - DWARF-CICHLID (befor Ap. reitzigi)
Mato-Grosso - Area, B, Male 8cm, Female 5cm
♀ ▷ ♫ ◑ ☺ ☺ ⊞ 🖼 ➤ ◈ 🔲

S03387-4 Apistogramma borellii "OPAL" MALE
BORELLI-OPAL - DWARF-CICHLID
Mato-Grosso - Area, B, Male 8cm, Female 5cm
♂ ▷ ♫ ◑ ☺ ☺ ⊞ 🖼 ➤ ◈ 🔲

S03387-4 Apistogramma borellii "OPAL" FEMALE with Babies !
BORELLI-OPAL - DWARF-CICHLID
Mato-Grosso - Area, B, Male 8cm, Female 5cm
♀ ▷ ♫ ◑ ☺ ☺ ⊞ 🖼 ➤ ◈ 🔲

S03384-4 Apistogramma borellii "CROSS" MALE
BORELLI-CROSS - DWARF-CICHLID cross-breeded
Mato-Grosso - Area, Z, Male 8cm, Female 5cm
♂ ▷ ♫ ◑ ☺ ☺ ⊞ 🖼 ➤ ◈ 🔲

© A.C.S. Glaser GmbH

S03386-3 Apistogramma borellii "PANTANAL" MALE
PANTANAL - DWARF-CICHLID
Pantanal, W, Male 8cm, Female 5cm

S03389-4 Apistogramma borellii "PARAGUAY" MALE
PARAGUAY - DWARF-CICHLID
Paraguay, W, Male 8cm, Female 7cm

S03389-4 Apistogramma borellii "PARAGUAY" FEMALE
PARAGUAY - DWARF-CICHLID
Paraguay, W, Male 8cm, Female 7cm

S03390-4 Apistogramma borellii "RED-HEAD" MALE
RED-HEAD - DWARF-CICHLID
Brazil, W, Male 8cm, Female 7cm

S03391-4 Apistogramma borellii "YELLOW-HEAD" MALE
YELLOW-HEAD - DWARF-CICHLID
Paraguay, W, Male 8cm, Female 7cm

S03395-3 Apistogramma cf. brevis MALE
BREVIS - DWARF-CICHLID
Uaupesi-Area Brazil, W, 4-5cm

S03400-3 Apistogramma cacatuoides MALE
BIG-MOUTH - APISTOGRAMMA
Amazonas-Area, W, Male 9cm + Female 5cm

S03400-3 Apistogramma cacatuoides FEMALE
BIG-MOUTH - APISTOGRAMMA
Amazonas-Area, W, Male 9cm + Female 5cm

S03402-3 Apistogramma cacatuoides "BLUE" MALE
BIG-MOUTH - APISTOGRAMMA
Amazonas-Area, W, Male 9cm + Female 5cm

♂ ▷ ♪ ◑ ☺ ☺ 🎴 🖼 🐟 ◈ 🔲

S03402-3 Apistogramma cacatuoides "BLUE" FEMALE
BIG-MOUTH - APISTOGRAMMA
Amazonas-Area, W, Male 9cm + Female 5cm

♀ ▷ ♪ ◑ ☺ ☺ 🎴 🖼 🐟 ◈ 🔲

S03404-4 Apistogramma cacatuoides "DOUBLE-RED" MALE
BIG-MOUTH - APISTOGRAMMA
Amazonas-Area, Z, Male 9cm + Female 5cm

♂ ▷ ♪ ◑ ☺ ☺ 🎴 🖼 🐟 ◈ 🔲

S03404-4 Apistogramma cacatuoides "DOUBLE-RED" FEMALE
BIG-MOUTH - APISTOGRAMMA
Amazonas-Area, Z, Male 9cm + Female 5cm

♀ ▷ ♪ ◑ ☺ ☺ 🎴 🖼 🐟 ◈ 🔲

S03406-2 Apistogramma cacatuoides "GOLD-ORANGE"
BIG-MOUTH - APISTOGRAMMA JUVENIL
Amazonas-Area, Z, Male 9cm + Female 5cm

▷ ♪ ◑ ☺ ☺ 🎴 🖼 🐟 ◈ 🔲

S03406-4 Apistogramma cacatuoides "GOLD-ORANGE"
BIG-MOUTH - APISTOGRAMMA MALE
Amazonas-Area, Z, Male 9cm + Female 5cm

♂ ▷ ♪ ◑ ☺ ☺ 🎴 🖼 🐟 ◈ 🔲

S03408-4 Apistogramma cacatuoides "PERU" MALE
BIG-MOUTH - APISTOGRAMMA
Peru, W, Male 8cm + Female 7cm

♂ ▷ ♪ ◑ ☺ ☺ 🎴 🖼 🐟 ◈ 🔲

S03412-4 Apistogramma cacatuoides "RED-FLASH"
BIG-MOUTH - APISTOGRAMMA MALE
Amazonas-Area, Z, Male 9cm + Female 5cm

♂ ▷ ♪ ◑ ☺ ☺ 🎴 🖼 🐟 ◈ 🔲

S03412-4 Apistogramma cacatuoides "RED-FLASH"
BIG-MOUTH - APISTOGRAMMA FEMALE
Amazonas-Area, Z, Male 9cm + Female 5cm

S03416-4 Apistogramma cacatuoides "REDTAIL"
BIG-MOUTH - APISTOGRAMMA MALE
Amazonas-Area, Z, Male 9cm + Female 5cm

S03416-4 Apistogramma cacatuoides "REDTAIL"
BIG-MOUTH - APISTOGRAMMA FEMALE with babies
Amazonas-Area, Z, Male 9cm + Female 5cm

S03417-4 Apistogramma cacatuoides "REDTAIL-SUPER"
BIG-MOUTH - APISTOGRAMMA MALE
Amazonas-Area, Z, Male 9cm + Female 5cm

S03417-4 Apistogramma cacatuoides "REDTAIL-SUPER"
BIG-MOUTH - APISTOGRAMMA FEMALE
Amazonas-Area, Z, Male 9cm + Female 5cm

S03418-4 Apistogramma cacatuoides "(CS)"
BIG-MOUTH - APISTOGRAMMA MALE
Amazonas-Area, Z, Male 9cm + Female 5cm

S03418-4 Apistogramma cacatuoides "(CS)"
BIG-MOUTH - APISTOGRAMMA MALE
Amazonas-Area, Z, Male 9cm + Female 5cm

S03418-4 Apistogramma cacatuoides "(CS)"
BIG-MOUTH - APISTOGRAMMA FEMALE with babies
Amazonas-Area, Z, Male 9cm + Female 5cm

S03420-4 Apistogramma cacatuoides "EAST"
BIG-MOUTH - APISTOGRAMMA   MALE
Amazonas-Area, Z, Male 9cm + Female 5cm
♂ ▷ ♗ ◑ ☺ ☻ ⊞ 🖼 🐟 ◈ 🔲

S03420-4 Apistogramma cacatuoides "EAST"
BIG-MOUTH - APISTOGRAMMA   FEMALE with spawn
Amazonas-Area, Z, Male 9cm + Female 5cm
♀ ▷ ♗ ◑ ☺ ☻ ⊞ 🖼 🐟 ◈ 🔲

S03430-3 Apistogramma caetei MALE
CAETE - DWARF-CICHLID
Rio Caete + Rio Apeo - Area Brazil, W, Male 6 + Fem.4cm
♂ ▷ ♗ ◑ ☺ ☻ ⊞ 🖼 🐟 ◈ 🔲

S03430-3 Apistogramma caetei MALE
CAETE - DWARF-CICHLID
Rio Caete + Rio Apeo - Area Brazil, W, Male 6 + Fem.4cm
♂ ▷ ♗ ◑ ☺ ☻ ⊞ 🖼 🐟 ◈ 🔲

S03430-3 Apistogramma caetei MALE brood-nursing !
CAETE - DWARF-CICHLID
Rio Caete + Rio Apeo - Area Brazil, W, Male 6 + Fem.4cm
♂ ▷ ♗ ◑ ☺ ☻ ⊞ 🖼 🐟 ◈ 🔲

S03432-3 Apistogramma caetei "BELEM" MALE
BELEM - DWARF-CICHLID
Brazil, W, Male 6 + Fem.4cm
♂ ▷ ♗ ◑ ☺ ☻ ⊞ 🖼 🐟 ◈ 🔲

S03435-3 Apistogramma sp. "BLUE-HEAD"   MALE
BLUE-HEAD - DWARF-CICHLID
Rio Apeo - Area Brazil, W, Male 6 + Female 4cm
♂ ▷ ♗ ◑ ☺ ☻ ⊞ 🖼 🐟 ◈ 🔲

S03435-3 Apistogramma sp. "BLUE-HEAD"   FEMALE
BLUE-HEAD - DWARF-CICHLID
Rio Apeo - Area Brazil, W, Male 6 + Female 4cm
♀ ▷ ♗ ◑ ☺ ☻ ⊞ 🖼 🐟 ◈ 🔲

© A.C.S. Glaser GmbH

S03445-3 Apistogramma commbrae MALE
COMMBRAE - DWARF-CICHLID
Brazil+Paraguay Asuncion-Corumba, W, 4-5cm

S03445-3 Apistogramma commbrae MALE
COMMBRAE - DWARF-CICHLID
Brazil+Paraguay Asuncion-Corumba, W, 4-5cm

S03445-4 Apistogramma commbrae PAIR
COMMBRAE - DWARF-CICHLID
Brazil+Paraguay Asuncion-Corumba, W, 4-5cm

S03455-4 Apistogramma cruzi MALE
CRUZI - DWARF-CICHLID
Amaz.-AREA Brazil/Columbia/Peru, W, M 8cm+F 5cm

S03455-4 Apistogramma cruzi FEMALE
CRUZI - DWARF-CICHLID
Amaz.-AREA Brazil/Columbia/Peru, W, M (CM*F 5cm

S03455-4 Apistogramma cruzi FEMALE at brood-nursing !
CRUZI - DWARF-CICHLID
Amaz.-AREA Brazil/Columbia/Peru, W, M (CM*F 5cm

S03457-3 Apistogramma cruzi "RIO-NAPO" MALE
RIO-NAPO - CRUZI-DWARF-CICHLID
Amaz.-AREA Brazil/Columbia/Peru, W, M (CM*F 5cm

S03457-3 Apistogramma cruzi "RIO-NAPO" FEMALE
RIO-NAPO - CRUZI-DWARF-CICHLID
Amaz.-AREA Brazil/Columbia/Peru, W, M (CM*F 5cm

S03457-3 Apistogramma cruzi   "RIO-NAPO"   FEMALE
RIO-NEGRO - CRUZI-DWARF-CICHLID   shock-reaction !
Amaz.-AREA Brazil/Columbia/Peru, W, M (CM*F 5cm

S03459-4 Apistogramma cf. cruzi   MALE
CRUZI - DWARF-CICHLID BREEDING
Amaz.-Area Brazil/Columbia/Peru, B, M 8cm+F 5cm

S03459-4 Apistogramma cf. cruzi   FEMALE
CRUZI - DWARF-CICHLID BREEDING
Amaz.-Area Brazil/Columbia/Peru, B, M 8cm+F 5cm

S03459-4 Apistogramma cf. cruzi   PAIR
CRUZI - DWARF-CICHLID BREEDING
Amaz.-Area Brazil/Columbia/Peru, B, M 8cm+F 5cm

S03465-4 Apistogramma diplotaenia   MALE
DOUBLE-BANDED - APISTOGRAMMA BREEDING
Rio-Negro, upper-Orinoco-System, B, M. 6 cm + F.4cm

S03465-2 Apistogramma diplotaenia   JUVENIL
DOUBLE-BANDED - APISTOGRAMMA BREEDING
Rio-Negro, upper-Orinoco-System, B, M. 6 cm + F.4cm

S03466-3 Apistogramma diplotaenia   MALE
DOUBLE-BANDED - APISTOGRAMMA
Rio-Negro, upper-Orinoco-System, W, M. 6 cm + F.4cm

S03466-3 Apistogramma diplotaenia   FEMALE
DOUBLE-BANDED - APISTOGRAMMA
Rio-Negro, upper-Orinoco-System, W, M. 6 cm + F.4cm

© A.C.S. Glaser GmbH

APISTOGRAMMA CRUZI "BREEDING-FEMALE"

S03468-3 Apistogramma diplotaenia "URUBAXI"
DOUBLE-BANDED - APISTOGRAMMA BREEDING
Rio-Urubaxi, , W, Male 6 cm + Female 4cm

S03475-3 Apistogramma elizabethae MALE
ELIZABETH - DWARF-CICHLID TYPUSLOCALITY
Brazil, W, 6-8cm

S03475-3 Apistogramma elizabethae FEMALE
ELIZABETH - DWARF-CICHLID TYPUSLOCALITY
Brazil, W, 6-8cm

S03480-4 Apistogramma elizabethae "BLUE" MALE
BLUE-ELIZABETH - DWARF-CICHLID
Brazil, W, 6-8cm

S03485-3 Apistogramma elizabethae "RED" MALE
RED-ELIZABETH - DWARF-CICHLID
Brazil, W, 6-8cm

S03487-4 Apistogramma elizabethae "RIO-UAUPES" MALE
UAUPES-ELIZABETH - DWARF-CICHLID
Brazil, W, 6-8cm

S03487-4 Apistogramma elizabethae "RIO-UAUPES" FEMALE
UAUPES-ELIZABETH   Brutpflege/brood-nursing !
Rio-Uaupes / Brazil, W, 6-8cm

S03490-3 Apistogramma elizabethae "WHITE" MALE
WHITE-ELIZABETH - DWARF-CICHLID
Brazil, B, 6-8cm

© A.C.S. Glaser GmbH

S03495-4 Apistogramma elizabethae "YELLOW" MALE
YELLOW-ELIZABETH - DWARF-CICHLID
Brazil, B, 6-8cm
♂ ▷ 🜨 ◑ ☺ ☺ ⊞ 🏞 ➤ ◈ 🅜

S03475-3 Apistogramma elizabethae PAIR balzend/mating !
ELIZABETH - DWARF-CICHLID Typuslocality !
Rio-Uaupes/Brazil, B, 6-8cm
♂ ♀ ▷ 🜨 ◑ ☺ ☺ ⊞ 🏞 ➤ ◈ 🅜

S03505-3 Apistogramma eunotus MALE
EUNOTUS - DWARF-CICHLID
Rio-Ucayali - Area/Peru, W, Male 8-9cm + Fem. 5-6cm
♂ ▷ 🜨 ◑ ☺ ☺ ⊞ 🏞 ➤ ◈ 🅜

S03505-3 Apistogramma eunotus FEMALE
EUNOTUS - DWARF-CICHLID
Rio-Ucayali - Area/Peru, W, Male 8-9cm + Fem. 5-6cm
♀ ▷ 🜨 ◑ ☺ ☺ ⊞ 🏞 ➤ ◈ 🅜

S03506-4 Apistogramma cf. eunotus MALE
EUNOTUS - DWARF-CICHLID
Rio-Ucayali - Area/Peru, B, Male 8-9cm + Fem. 5-6cm
♂ ▷ 🜨 ◑ ☺ ☺ ⊞ 🏞 ➤ ◈ 🅜

S03506-4 Apistogramma cf. eunotus FEMALE
EUNOTUS - DWARF-CICHLID
Rio-Ucayali - Area/Peru, B, Male 8-9cm + Fem. 5-6cm
♀ ▷ 🜨 ◑ ☺ ☺ ⊞ 🏞 ➤ ◈ 🅜

S03520-3 Apistogramma geisleri MALE
GEISLER - DWARF-CICHLID
Unterlauf/lower-course of Amazonas, W, 5-7cm
♂ ▷ 🜨 ◑ ☺ ☺ ⊞ 🏞 ➤ ◈ 🅜

S03520-3 Apistogramma geisleri FEMALE
GEISLER - DWARF-CICHLID
Unterlauf/lower-course of Amazonas, W, 5-7cm
♀ ▷ 🜨 ◑ ☺ ☺ ⊞ 🏞 ➤ ◈ 🅜

APISTOGRAMMA GEPHYRA "BLUE" MALE

© **A.C.S. Glaser GmbH**

APISTOGRAMMA HOIGNEI "BREEDING-FORM"

S03522-4 Apistogramma sp. aff. geisleri MALE
GEISLER - DWARF-CICHLID
Unterlauf/lower-course of Amazonas, W, 5-7cm

♂ ▷ ♫ ◐ ☺ ☺ 🔲 🖼 ➡ ◈ 🔟

S03525-4 Apistogramma gephyra MALE
GEPHYRA - DWARF-CICHLID
Amazonas(Manaus-Santarem), W, M. 6cm + F. 4cm

♂ ▷ ♫ ◐ ☺ ☺ 🔲 🖼 ➡ ◈ 🔟

S03525-4 Apistogramma gephyra FEMALE
GEPHYRA - DWARF-CICHLID
Amazonas(Manaus-Santarem), W, M. 6cm + F. 4cm

♀ ▷ ♫ ◐ ☺ ☺ 🔲 🖼 ➡ ◈ 🔟

S03525-3 Apistogramma gephyra PAIR
GEPHYRA - DWARF-CICHLID
Amazonas(Manaus-Santarem), W, M. 6cm + F. 4cm

♂ ♀ ▷ ♫ ◐ ☺ ☺ 🔲 🖼 ➡ ◈ 🔟

S03526-4 Apistogramma gephyra "RIO-NEGRO" MALE
GEPHYRA - DWARF-CICHLID
Barcelus/Rio-Negro/Brazil, W, M. 6cm + F. 4cm

♂ ▷ ♫ ◐ ☺ ☺ 🔲 🖼 ➡ ◈ 🔟

S03526-4 Apistogramma gephyra "RIO-NEGRO" FEMALE
GEPHYRA - DWARF-CICHLID
Barcelus/Rio-Negro/Brazil, W, M. 6cm + F. 4cm

♀ ▷ ♫ ◐ ☺ ☺ 🔲 🖼 ➡ ◈ 🔟

S03528-4 Apistogramma gephyra "BLACK-BAND" MALE
BLACK-BAND - DWARF-CICHLID
Amazonas-Area/Brazil, W, M. 6cm + F. 4cm

♂ ▷ ♫ ◐ ☺ ☺ 🔲 🖼 ➡ ◈ 🔟

S03530-4 Apistogramma gephyra "BLUE" MALE
BLUE-GEPHYRA - DWARF-CICHLID
Amazonas-Area/Brazil, W, M. 6cm + F. 4cm

♂ ▷ ♫ ◐ ☺ ☺ 🔲 🖼 ➡ ◈ 🔟

© A.C.S. Glaser GmbH

S03535-3 Apistogramma gibbiceps   MALE
GIBBICEPS - DWARF-CICHLID
Rio-Negro - Area/Brazil, W, Male 8cm + Female 6cm
♂ ▷ ♬ ◑ ☺ ☺ ⊞ 🖼 🦐 ◈ m

S03535-3 Apistogramma gibbiceps   FEMALE
GIBBICEPS - DWARF-CICHLID
Rio-Negro - Area/Brazil, W, Male 8cm + Female 6cm
♀ ▷ ♬ ◑ ☺ ☺ ⊞ 🖼 🦐 ◈ m

S03538-3 Apistogramma cf. gibbiceps   MALE
BLUE-GIBBICEPS - DWARF-CICHLID
Rio-Negro/Barcelos/Brazil, W, Male 8cm + Female 6cm
♂ ▷ ♬ ◑ ☺ ☺ ⊞ 🖼 🦐 ◈ m

S03538-3 Apistogramma cf. gibbiceps   FEMALE
BLUE-GIBBICEPS - DWARF-CICHLID
Rio-Negro/Barcelos/Brazil, W, Male 8cm + Female 6cm
♀ ▷ ♬ ◑ ☺ ☺ ⊞ 🖼 🦐 ◈ m

S03540-3 Apistogramma cf. gibbiceps "YELLOW" MALE
YELLOW-GIBBICEPS - DWARF-CICHLID
Brazil, B, Male 8cm + Female 6cm
♂ ▷ ♬ ◑ ☺ ☺ ⊞ 🖼 🦐 ◈ m

S03540-3 Apistogramma cf. gibbiceps "YELLOW" FEMALE
YELLOW-GIBBICEPS - DWARF-CICHLID
Brazil, B, Male 8cm + Female 6cm
♀ ▷ ♬ ◑ ☺ ☺ ⊞ 🖼 🦐 ◈ m

S03545-3 Apistogramma gossei MALE
GOSSEI - DWARF-CICHLID
Franz.Guayana, W, 7-8cm
♂ ▷ ♬ ◑ ☺ ☺ ⊞ 🖼 🦐 ◈ m

S03545-3 Apistogramma gossei FEMALE
GOSSEI - DWARF-CICHLID
Franz.Guayana, W, 7-8cm
♀ ▷ ♬ ◑ ☺ ☺ ⊞ 🖼 🦐 ◈ m

S03550-4 Apistogramma guttata MALE
GUTTATA - DWARF-CICHLID
Rio Morichal/Venezuela, W, 5cm

S03550-4 Apistogramma guttata FEMALE
GUTTATA - DWARF-CICHLID
Rio Morichal/Venezuela, W, 5cm

S03560-3 Apistogramma hippolytae MALE
HIPPO - DWARF-CICHLID
Lago-Manacapuru/Brazil, W, Male 6-7cm + Fem.4-5cm

S03560-3 Apistogramma hippolytae MALE
HIPPO - DWARF-CICHLID
Lago-Manacapuru/Brazil, W, Male 6-7cm + Fem.4-5cm

S03565-3 Apistogramma hoignei MALE
HOIGNEI - DWARF-CICHLID W, 7-8cm
Unterlauf/lower course of Rio Portoguesa/Venezuela

S03565-3 Apistogramma hoignei FEMALE with larves
HOIGNEI - DWARF-CICHLID W, 7-8cm
Unterlauf/lower course of Rio Portoguesa/Venezuela

S03565-3 Apistogramma hoignei FEMALE with babies !
HOIGNEI - DWARF-CICHLID W, 7-8cm
Unterlauf/lower course of Rio Portoguesa/Venezuela

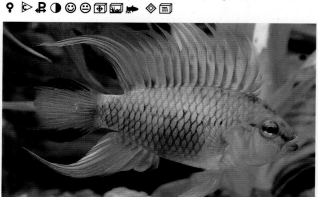

S03566-4 Apistogramma hoignei "BREEDING-FORM"   MALE
HOIGNEI - DWARF-CICHLID B, 7-8cm
Unterlauf/lower course of Rio Portoguesa/Venezuela

© A.C.S. Glaser GmbH

1. Biotop/Typuslocality of Apistogramma mendezi

Foto: **im Jahre 1991** / *photo: in the year 1991*

2. Das selbe Biotop, fotografiert 1 Jahr später im Jahre 1992.

The same biotope, photographed on year later in 1992.

APISTOGRAMMA HOIGNEI "VENEZUELA"

© A.C.S. Glaser GmbH

S03568-3 Apistogramma hoignei "ORINOCO" MALE
HOIGNEI - DWARF-CICHLID
middle of Orinoco/Venezuela, W, 6-7cm

♂ ▷ 🕮 ◐ ☺ ☺ ⊞ 🖼 ➡ ◈ 🔟

S03568-3 Apistogramma hoignei "ORINOCO" FEMALE
HOIGNEI - DWARF-CICHLID
middle of Orinoco/Venezuela, W, 6-7cm

♀ ▷ 🕮 ◐ ☺ ☺ ⊞ 🖼 ➡ ◈ 🔟

S03569-4 Apistogramma hoignei "GOLDHEAD" MALE
GOLDHEAD-HOIGNEI - DWARF-CICHLID
Orinoco/Venezuela, W, 7-8cm

♂ ▷ 🕮 ◐ ☺ ☺ ⊞ 🖼 ➡ ◈ 🔟

S03570-4 Apistogramma hoignei "TUCUPITA" MALE
TUCUPITA - DWARF-CICHLID
Orinoco-Delta/Tucupita/Venezue, W, 7-8cm

♂ ▷ 🕮 ◐ ☺ ☺ ⊞ 🖼 ➡ ◈ 🔟

S03581-4 Apistogramma cf. hongsloi VENEZUELA MALE
HONGSLOI - DWARF(similar sp.REDSTROKE) M. 7-8cm
middle of Orinoco/Columbia/Venezuela, W, F. 4-5cm

♂ ▷ 🕮 ◐ ☺ ☺ ⊞ 🖼 ➡ ◈ 🔟

S03580-4 Apistogramma hongsloi FEMALE
HONGSLOI - DWARF (similar sp.REDSTROKE) M. 7-8cm
middle of Orinoco/Columbia/Venezuela, W, F. 4-5cm

♀ ▷ 🕮 ◐ ☺ ☺ ⊞ 🖼 ➡ ◈ 🔟

S03584-3 Apistogramma hongsloi "GOLD-FORM" MALE
GOLD-HONGSLOI - DWARF-CICHLID
Venezuela, W, 6-7cm

♂ ▷ 🕮 ◐ ☺ ☺ ⊞ 🖼 ➡ ◈ 🔟

S03584-3 Apistogramma hongsloi "GOLD-FORM" FEMALE
GOLD-HONGSLOI - DWARF-CICHLID
Venezuela, W, 6-7cm

♀ ▷ 🕮 ◐ ☺ ☺ ⊞ 🖼 ➡ ◈ 🔟

S03582-4 Apistogramma hongsloi "EAST-BREEDING" MALE
EAST-HONGSLOI - DWARF-CICHLID
Venezuela, B, 6-7cm

S03588-4 Apistogramma hongsloi I WILD-FORM MALE
HONGSLOI I - DWARF-CICHLID
Venezuela, W, 6-7cm

S03588-4 Apistogramma hongsloi I WILD-FORM PAIR
HONGSLOI I - DWARF-CICHLID
Venezuela, W, 6-7cm

S03589-4 Apistogramma hongsloi I BREEDING MALE
HONGSLOI I - DWARF-CICHLID
Venezuela, W, 6-7cm

S03589-4 Apistogramma hongsloi I BREEDING FEMALE
HONGSLOI I - DWARF-CICHLID
Venezuela, W, 6-7cm

S03590-4 Apistogramma hongsloi II WILD-FORM MALE
HONGSLOI II - DWARF-CICHLID
Venezuela, W, 6-7cm

S03591-4 Apistogramma hongsloi II BREEDING MALE
HONGSLOI II - DWARF-CICHLID
Venezuela, W, 6-7cm

S03592-5 Apistogramma hongsloi II MALE
HONGSLOI II DWARF "SUPER-WINNER AQUARAMA 95"
Venezuela, Z, 8-9cm

© A.C.S. Glaser GmbH

S03600-4 Apistogramma inconspicua MALE
INCONSPICUA - DWARF-CICHLID Höhlen/den-breeder !
Bolivia/Paraguay/Brazil, W, 7-8cm
♂ ▷ ♫ ◑ ☺ ☻ ⊞ 🖼 ➤ ◈ ㎜

S03600-4 Apistogramma inconspicua FEMALE
INCONSPICUA - DWARF-CICHLID Höhlen/den-breeder !
Bolivia/Paraguay/Brazil, W, 7-8cm
♀ ▷ ♫ ◑ ☺ ☻ ⊞ 🖼 ➤ ◈ ㎜

S03605-3 Apistogramma iniridae MALE
INIRIDA - DWARF-CICHLID
Rio-Iniridae-Area/Columbia, W, Male 6-7 + Fem.4-5cm
♂ ▷ ♫ ◑ ☺ ☻ ⊞ 🖼 ➤ ◈ ㎜

S03605-3 Apistogramma iniridae FEMALE
INIRIDA - DWARF-CICHLID
Rio-Iniridae-Area/Columbia, W, Male 6-7 + Fem.4-5cm
♀ ▷ ♫ ◑ ☺ ☻ ⊞ 🖼 ➤ ◈ ㎜

S03606-4 Apistogramma iniridae MALE
INIRIDA - DWARF-CICHLID   BREEDING-FORM
Rio-Iniridae-Area/Columbia, B, Male 6-7 + Fem.4-5cm
♂ ▷ ♫ ◑ ☺ ☻ ⊞ 🖼 ➤ ◈ ㎜

S03606-4 Apistogramma iniridae FEMALE
INIRIDA - DWARF-CICHLID   BREEDING-FORM
Rio-Iniridae-Area/Columbia, B, Male 6-7 + Fem.4-5cm
♀ ▷ ♫ ◑ ☺ ☻ ⊞ 🖼 ➤ ◈ ㎜

S03615-4 Apistogramma juruensis MALE
JURUA - DWARF-CICHLID
Riio-Jurua/Brazil, W, 8-10cm
♂ ▷ ♫ ◑ ☺ ☻ ⊞ 🖼 ➤ ◈ ㎜

S03615-4 Apistogramma juruensis FEMALE
JURUA - DWARF-CICHLID
Riio-Jurua/Brazil, W, 8-10cm
♀ ▷ ♫ ◑ ☺ ☻ ⊞ 🖼 ➤ ◈ ㎜

APISTOGRAMMA HONGSLOI I

APISTOGRAMMA HONGSLOI II

© A.C.S. Glaser GmbH

S03615-4 Apistogramma juruensis MALE
JURUA - DWARF-CICHLID
Riio-Jurua/Brazil, W, 8-10cm
♂ ▷ ♫ ◑ ☺ ☻ ⊞ 🖼 ➤ ◈ 🔟

S03615-4 Apistogramma juruensis FEMALE
JURUA - DWARF-CICHLID
Riio-Jurua/Brazil, W, 8-10cm
♀ ▷ ♫ ◑ ☺ ☻ ⊞ 🖼 ➤ ◈ 🔟

S03615-4 Apistogramma juruensis MALE
JURUA - DWARF-CICHLID
Riio-Jurua/Brazil, W, 8-10cm
♂ ▷ ♫ ◑ ☺ ☻ ⊞ 🖼 ➤ ◈ 🔟

S03615-4 Apistogramma juruensis FEMALE
JURUA - DWARF-CICHLID
Riio-Jurua/Brazil, W, 8-10cm
♀ ▷ ♫ ◑ ☺ ☻ ⊞ 🖼 ➤ ◈ 🔟

S03625-4 Apistogramma linkei MALE
LINKE - DWARF-CICHLID
Santa Cruz-Area/Bolivia, W, Male 6cm + Female 4cm
♂ ▷ ♫ ◑ ☺ ☻ ⊞ 🖼 ➤ ◈ 🔟

S03625-4 Apistogramma linkei FEMALE with babies
LINKE - DWARF-CICHLID
Santa Cruz-Area/Bolivia, W, Male 6cm + Female 4cm
♀ ▷ ♫ ◑ ☺ ☻ ⊞ 🖼 ➤ ◈ 🔟

S03626-3 Apistogramma linkei MALE
LINKE - DWARF-CICHLID SOUTHERN-FORM
Santa Cruz-Area/Bolivia, W, Male 6cm + Female 4cm
♂ ▷ ♫ ◑ ☺ ☻ ⊞ 🖼 ➤ ◈ 🔟

S03626-3 Apistogramma linkei FEMALE
LINKE - DWARF-CICHLID SOUTHERN-FORM
Santa Cruz-Area/Bolivia, W, Male 6cm + Female 4cm
♀ ▷ ♫ ◑ ☺ ☻ ⊞ 🖼 ➤ ◈ 🔟

S03627-4 Apistogramma linkei MALE
LINKE - DWARF-CICHLID   BREEDING-FORM
Santa Cruz-Area/Bolivia, B, Male 6cm + Female 4cm

♂ ▷ ♫ ◑ ☺ ☺ ⊞ 🖼 ➠ ◈ 🔳

S03627-3 Apistogramma linkei FEMALE
LINKE - DWARF-CICHLID   BREEDING-FORM
Santa Cruz-Area/Bolivia, B, Male 6cm + Female 4cm

♀ ▷ ♫ ◑ ☺ ☺ ⊞ 🖼 ➠ ◈ 🔳

S03635-3 Apistogramma luelingi   MALE
LUELING - DWARF-CICHLID
Rio Chapore+Chipiri - Area/Bolivia, W, M. 7cm + F.4cm

♂ ▷ ♫ ◑ ☺ ☺ ⊞ 🖼 ➠ ◈ 🔳

S03635-3 Apistogramma luelingi   FEMALE
LUELING - DWARF-CICHLID
Rio Chapore+Chipiri - Area/Bolivia, W, M. 7cm + F.4cm

♀ ▷ ♫ ◑ ☺ ☺ ⊞ 🖼 ➠ ◈ 🔳

S03636-4 Apistogramma luelingi   MALE
LUELING - DWARF-CICHLID   BREEDING-FORM
Rio Chapore+Chipiri - Area/Bolivia, B, M. 7cm + F.4cm

♂ ▷ ♫ ◑ ☺ ☺ ⊞ 🖼 ➠ ◈ 🔳

S03636-4 Apistogramma luelingi   FEMALE
LUELING - DWARF-CICHLID   BREEDING-FORM
Rio Chapore+Chipiri - Area/Bolivia, B, M. 7cm + F.4cm

♀ ▷ ♫ ◑ ☺ ☺ ⊞ 🖼 ➠ ◈ 🔳

S03635-3 Apistogramma luelingi   MALE
LUELING - DWARF-CICHLID
Rio Chapore+Chipiri - Area/Bolivia, M. 7cm + F.4cm

♂ ▷ ♫ ◑ ☺ ☺ ⊞ 🖼 ➠ ◈ 🔳

S03635-3 Apistogramma luelingi   FEMALE
LUELING - DWARF-CICHLID
Rio Chapore+Chipiri - Area/Bolivia, M. 7cm + F.4cm

♀ ▷ ♫ ◑ ☺ ☺ ⊞ 🖼 ➠ ◈ 🔳

© A.C.S. Glaser GmbH

S03650-2 Apistogramma macmasteri JUVENIL
MACMASTER - DWARF-CICHLID
Rio Meta+Orinoco/Columbia, W, 7-8cm

S03650-3 Apistogramma macmasteri MALE
MACMASTER - DWARF-CICHLID
Rio Meta+Orinoco/Columbia, W, 7-8cm

S03650-3 Apistogramma macmasteri FEMALE
MACMASTER - DWARF-CICHLID   SEMIADULT
Rio Meta+Orinoco/Columbia, W, 7-8cm

S03650-4 Apistogramma macmasteri MALE
MACMASTER - DWARF-CICHLID
Rio Meta+Orinoco/Columbia, W, 7-8cm

S03650-4 Apistogramma macmasteri FEMALE
MACMASTER - DWARF-CICHLID
Rio Meta+Orinoco/Columbia, W, 7-8cm

S03652-5 Apistogramma macmasteri MALE
MACMASTER - DWARF-CICHLID   BREEDING-FORM
Rio Meta+Orinoco/Columbia, Z, 7-8cm

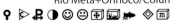

S03652-5 Apistogramma macmasteri FEMALE
MACMASTER - DWARF-CICHLID   BREEDING-FORM
Rio Meta+Orinoco/Columbia, Z, 7-8cm

S03654-4 Apistogramma macmasteri "RED-SPOT" MALE
MACMASTER - DWARF-CICHLID
Rio Meta+Orinoco/Columbia, B, 7-8cm

S03656-4 Apistogramma macmasteri "BLUEHEAD" MALE
MACMASTER - DWARF-CICHLID
Rio Meta+Orinoco/Columbia, B, 7-8cm
♂ ▷ ♠ ◑ ☺ ☺ ⊞ 🖼 ➟ ◈ 🔟

S03670-4 Apistogramma macmasteri "REDTAIL" MALE
MACMASTER - DWARF-CICHLID
Rio Meta+Orinoco/Columbia, Z, 7-8cm
♂ ▷ ♠ ◑ ☺ ☺ ⊞ 🖼 ➟ ◈ 🔟

S03670-4 Apistogramma macmasteri "REDTAIL" FEMALE
MACMASTER - DWARF-CICHLID
Rio Meta+Orinoco/Columbia, Z, 7-8cm
♀ ▷ ♠ ◑ ☺ ☺ ⊞ 🖼 ➟ ◈ 🔟

S03652-4 Apistogramma macmasteri MALE
MACMASTER - DWARF-CICHLID
Rio Meta+Orinoco/Columbia, Z, 7-8cm
♂ ▷ ♠ ◑ ☺ ☺ ⊞ 🖼 ➟ ◈ 🔟

S03665-3 Apistogramma macmasteri "GAITAN" MALE
MACMASTER - DWARF-CICHLID
Puerto Gaitan, Rio-Meta/Columbia , 6-7cm
♂ ▷ ♠ ◑ ☺ ☺ ⊞ 🖼 ➟ ◈ 🔟

S03665-3 Apistogramma macmasteri "GAITAN" FEMALE
MACMASTER - DWARF-CICHLID
Puerto Gaitan, Rio-Meta/Columbia , W, 6-7cm
♀ ▷ ♠ ◑ ☺ ☺ ⊞ 🖼 ➟ ◈ 🔟

S03677-3 Apistogramma macmasteri "VILLAVICENCIO" MALE
MACMASTER - DWARF-CICHLID
Villavicencio/Rio-Meta/Columbia , W, 6-7cm
♂ ▷ ♠ ◑ ☺ ☺ ⊞ 🖼 ➟ ◈ 🔟

S03677-3 Apistogramma macmasteri "VILLAVICENCIO" FEMALE
MACMASTER - DWARF-CICHLID
Villavicencio/Rio-Meta/Columbia , W, 6-7cm
♀ ▷ ♠ ◑ ☺ ☺ ⊞ 🖼 ➟ ◈ 🔟

© **A.C.S. Glaser GmbH**

APISTOGRAMMA JURUENSIS

S03675-4 Apistogramma macmasteri "TAME" MALE
MACMASTER - DWARF-CICHLID
Tame/Rio-Arauca/Columbia , W, 6-7cm

S03675-4 Apistogramma macmasteri "TAME" FEMALE
MACMASTER - DWARF-CICHLID
Tame/Rio-Arauca/Columbia , W, 6-7cm

S03685-4 Apistogramma meinkeni MALE
MEINKENI - DWARF-CICHLID
Rio Uaupes-Area/Brazil, W, Male 6-7cm + Fem. 4-5cm

S03685-4 Apistogramma meinkeni FEMALE
MEINKENI - DWARF-CICHLID
Rio Uaupes-Area/Brazil, W, Male 6-7cm + Fem. 4-5cm

S03685-3 Apistogramma meinkeni MALE
MEINKENI - DWARF-CICHLID
Rio Uaupes-Area/Brazil, W, Male 6-7cm + Fem. 4-5cm

S03685-3 Apistogramma meinkeni FEMALE
MEINKENI - DWARF-CICHLID
Rio Uaupes-Area/Brazil, W, Male 6-7cm + Fem. 4-5cm

S03695-3 Apistogramma mendezi MALE
MENDEZI - DWARF-CICHLID
Rio-Negro/Brazil, W, 8-10cm

S03695-3 Apistogramma mendezi FEMALE
MENDEZI - DWARF-CICHLID
Rio-Negro/Brazil, W, 8-10cm

S03698-3 Apistogramma mendezi MALE   TYPUSLOCALITY
MENDEZI - DWARF-CICHLID   F 1 - Nachzucht
Rio-Negro/Brazil, W, 8-10cm   F 1 - breeding

♂ ▷ ♫ ◑ ☺ ☺ ⊞ ▦ ➤ ◈ ▥

S03698-3 Apistogramma mendezi FEMALE at aggressive-mood
MENDEZI - DWARF-CICHLID   TYPUSLOCALITY
Rio-Negro/Brazil, W, 8-10cm

♀ ▷ ♫ ◑ ☺ ☺ ⊞ ▦ ➤ ◈ ▥

S03701-3 Apistogramma mendezi "CURICURIARI" MALE
CURUCURARI - DWARF similar to A. sp. ROTKEIL !
Brazil, W, 8-10cm

♂ ▷ ♫ ◑ ☺ ☺ ⊞ ▦ ➤ ◈ ▥

S03701-3 Apistogramma mendezi "CURICURIARI"   FEMALE
CURUCURARI - DWARF similar to A. sp. ROTKEIL!
Brazil, W, 8-10cm

♀ ▷ ♫ ◑ ☺ ☺ ⊞ ▦ ➤ ◈ ▥

S03705-3 Apistogramma mendezi "MARIAE"   MALE
MARIAE - DWARF-CICHLID
Rio-Mariae, W, 8-10cm

♂ ▷ ♫ ◑ ☺ ☺ ⊞ ▦ ➤ ◈ ▥

S03705-3 Apistogramma mendezi "MARIAE"   FEMALE
MARIAE - DWARF-CICHLID
Rio-Mariae, W, 8-10cm

♀ ▷ ♫ ◑ ☺ ☺ ⊞ ▦ ➤ ◈ ▥

S03695-3 Apistogramma mendezi   beginnende Balz !
MENDEZI - DWARF-CICHLID beginning of mating !
Rio-Mariae, W, 8-10cm

▷ ♫ ◑ ☺ ☺ ⊞ ▦ ➤ ◈ ▥

S03715-3 Apistogramma moae
MOAE - DWARF-CICHLID
Rio Mao-Area/Brazil, W, Male 5-6 + Female 3-4cm

▷ ♫ ◑ ☺ ☺ ⊞ ▦ ➤ ◈ ▥

APISTOGRAMMA SP. MACMASTERI "LONGTAIL - BREEDING-FORM" MALE

APISTOGRAMMA SP. MACMASTERI "LONGTAIL - BREEDING-FORM" PAIR

© **A.C.S. Glaser GmbH**

S03725-4 Apistogramma nijsseni MALE
PANDA - DWARF-CICHLID
lower Area of Rio-Ucayali/Peru, W, M.7-8 + F.4-5cm
♂ ▷ ♫ ◑ ☺ ☻ ⊞ 🖼 ⇥ ◈ ▥

S03725-4 Apistogramma nijsseni FEMALE
PANDA - DWARF-CICHLID
lower Area of Rio-Ucayali/Peru, W, M.7-8 + F.4-5cm
♀ ▷ ♫ ◑ ☺ ☻ ⊞ 🖼 ⇥ ◈ ▥

S03725-4 Apistogramma nijsseni PAIR
PANDA - DWARF-CICHLID
lower Area of Rio-Ucayali/Peru, W, M.7-8 + F.4-5cm
♂ ♀ ▷ ♫ ◑ ☺ ☻ ⊞ 🖼 ⇥ ◈ ▥

S03725-4 Apistogramma nijsseni MALE
PANDA - DWARF-CICHLID
lower Area of Rio-Ucayali/Peru, W, M.7-8 + F.4-5cm
♂ ▷ ♫ ◑ ☺ ☻ ⊞ 🖼 ⇥ ◈ ▥

S03725-4 Apistogramma nijsseni Male
PANDA - DWARF-CICHLID
lower Area of Rio-Ucayali/Peru, B, M.7-8 + F.4-5cm
♂ ▷ ♫ ◑ ☺ ☻ ⊞ 🖼 ⇥ ◈ ▥

S03725-4 Apistogramma nijsseni FEMALE with spawn
PANDA- DWARF-CICHLID
lower Area of Rio-Ucayali/Peru, B, M.7-8 + F.4-5cm
♀ ▷ ♫ ◑ ☺ ☻ ⊞ 🖼 ⇥ ◈ ▥

S03740-3 Apistogramma norberti MALE
THICK-LIPS - APISTOGRAMMA
Rio Talinayo-Area/Peru, W, 6-7cm
♂ ▷ ♫ ◑ ☺ ☻ ⊞ 🖼 ⇥ ◈ ▥

S03740-3 Apistogramma norberti MALE
THICK-LIPS - APISTOGRAMMA
Rio Talinayo-Area/Peru, W, 6-7cm
♂ ▷ ♫ ◑ ☺ ☻ ⊞ 🖼 ⇥ ◈ ▥

S03740-3 Apistogramma norberti FEMALE in Brutpflege-Färbung
THICK-LIPS - APISTOGRAMMA   at brood-nurse-colour !
Rio Talinayo-Area/Peru, W, 6-7cm

S03742-2 Apistogramma norberti
THICK-LIPS - APISTOGRAMMA
Rio Talinayo-Area/Peru, B, 6-7cm

S03742-4 Apistogramma norberti MALE
THICK-LIPS - APISTOGRAMMA
Rio Talinayo-Area/Peru, B, 6-7cm

S03755-3 Apistogramma ortmanni MALE
ORTMANN - DWARF-CICHLID
Rio-Rupununi/Guayana, W, 7-8cm

S03755-4 Apistogramma ortmanni MALE
ORTMANN - DWARF-CICHLID
Rio-Rupununi/Guayana, W, 7-8cm

S03755-4 Apistogramma ortmanni MALE
ORTMANN - DWARF-CICHLID
Tumuremo-Stausee/resavoir Venezuela, W, 6-7cm

S03760-4 Apistogramma cf. ortmanni MALE
ORTMANN - DWARF-CICHLID
Cuyuni-Area/Venezuela, W, 6-7cm

S03770-3 Apistogramma paucisquamis MALE
PAUCIS - DWARF-CICHLID   same as sp. GLANZBINDEN !
Rio-Negro/Brazil, W, 6-8cm

© **A.C.S. Glaser GmbH**

S03770-3 Apistogramma paucisquamis FEMALE
PAUCIS - DWARF-CICHLID
Rio-Negro/Brazil, W, 6-8cm

S03780-3 Apistogramma personata "MITU" MALE
MITU - DWARF-CICHLID
Mitu/Rio Vaupes/Columbia, W, 6-7cm

S03785-4 Apistogramma pertensis MALE
PERTENSIS - DWARF-CICHLID
Amazonas Manacapuru-Santarem/Brazil, W, 5-6cm

S03786-4 Apistogramma cf. pertensis MALE
PERTENSIS - DWARF-CICHLID
Amazonas Manacapuru-Santarem/Brazil, W, 5-6cm

S03787-4 Apistogramma cf. pertensis "PRETO" MALE
PERTENSIS - DWARF-CICHLID
Rio-Preto/Brazil, W, 5-6cm

S03787-4 Apistogramma cf. pertensis "PRETO" MALE
PERTENSIS - DWARF-CICHLID
Rio-Preto/Brazil, W, 5-6cm

S03785-2 Apistogramma pertensis MALE
PERTENSIS - DWARF-CICHLID
Rio-Negro Brazil, W, 4-5cm   agressive-mood

S03785-2 Apistogramma pertensis MALE
PERTENSIS - DWARF-CICHLID
Rio-Negro Brazil, W, 4-5cm   agressive-mood

S03789-4 Apistogramma cf. pertensis "NEGRO" MALE
NEGRO-PERTENSIS - DWARF-CICHLID
Rio-Negro/Brazil, W, 6cm

S03793-3 Apistogramma sp. aff. pertensis "TAPAJOS" MALE
PERTENSIS - DWARF-CICHLID similar to A. meinkeni !
Rio-Tapajos/Brazil, W, 4-5cm

S03793-3 Apistogramma sp. aff. pertensis "TAPAJOS" FEMALE
PERTENSIS - DWARF-CICHLID similar to A. meinkeni !
Rio-Tapajos/Brazil, W, 4-5cm

S03795-4 Apistogramma piauensis MALE
PIAU - DWARF-CICHLID
Rio-Longa, W, 3-4cm

S03795-4 Apistogramma piauensis FEMALE
PIAU - DWARF-CICHLID
Rio-Longa, W, 3-4cm

S03800-4 Apistogramma pulchra MALE
PULCHRA - DWARF-CICHLID
Rio-Preto/Brazil, W, Male 5cm + Female 3cm

S03805-4 Apistogramma cf. pulchra MALE
PULCHRA - DWARF-CICHLID
Rio-Preto/Brazil, W, Male 5cm + Female 3cm

S03805-4 Apistogramma cf. pulchra FEMALE
PULCHRA - DWARF-CICHLID
Rio-Preto/Brazil, W, Male 5cm + Female 3cm

© A.C.S. Glaser GmbH

APISTOGRAMMA MENDEZI MALE

S03810-3 Apistogramma regani MALE
REGANI - DWARF-CICHLID   M.6-7cm
Rio Negro+Amazonas-Area,near Manaus/Brazil F.4-5cm

♂ ▷ ♬ ◐ ☺ ☺ ⊞ 🖼 🐟 ◈ m̄

S03810-3 Apistogramma regani FEMALE
REGANI - DWARF-CICHLID   M.6-7cm
Rio Negro+Amazonas-Area,near Manaus/Brazil F.4-5cm

♀ ▷ ♬ ◐ ☺ ☺ ⊞ 🖼 🐟 ◈ m̄

S03815-3 Apistogramma resticulosa
RESTI - DWARF-CICGHLID
Rio-Madeira/Brazil, W, Male 5cm + Female 3cm

▷ ♬ ◐ ☺ ☺ ⊞ 🖼 🐟 ◈ m̄

S03815-3 Apistogramma resticulosa
RESTI - DWARF-CICGHLID
Rio-Madeira/Brazil, W, Male 5cm + Female 3cm

▷ ♬ ◐ ☺ ☺ ⊞ 🖼 🐟 ◈ m̄

S03816-4 Apistogramma resticulosa MALE
RESTI - DWARF-CICGHLID
Rio-Madeira/Brazil, B, Male 5cm + Female 3cm

♂ ▷ ♬ ◐ ☺ ☺ ⊞ 🖼 🐟 ◈ m̄

S03816-4 Apistogramma resticulosa FEMALE
RESTI - DWARF-CICGHLID
Rio-Madeira/Brazil, B, Male 5cm + Female 3cm

♀ ▷ ♬ ◐ ☺ ☺ ⊞ 🖼 🐟 ◈ m̄

S03817-3 Apistogramma resticulosa "VELHO"
RESTI - DWARF-CICGHLID
Puerto-Velho/Brazil, W, Male 5cm + Female 3cm

▷ ♬ ◐ ☺ ☺ ⊞ 🖼 🐟 ◈ m̄

S03817-3 Apistogramma resticulosa "VELHO"
RESTI - DWARF-CICGHLID
Puerto-Velho/Brazil, W, Male 5cm + Female 3cm

▷ ♬ ◐ ☺ ☺ ⊞ 🖼 🐟 ◈ m̄

© **A.C.S. Glaser GmbH**

S03820-2 Apistogramma rupununi (before A.sp.2-spot) JUVENIL
RUPUNUNI - DWARF-CICHLID
Br.Guayana, W, 5-6cm
▷ ♬ ◑ ☺ ☺ ⊞ ▨ ➤ ◈ ▥

S03820-3 Apistogramma rupununi (before A.sp.2-spot MALE
RUPUNUNI - DWARF-CICHLID
Br.Guayana, W, 5-6cm
♂ ▷ ♬ ◑ ☺ ☺ ⊞ ▨ ➤ ◈ ▥

S03835-3 Apistogramma sp. "ALENQUER" MALE
ALENQUER - DWARF-CICHLID
Alenquer/Brazil, W, 5-6cm
♂ ▷ ♬ ◑ ☺ ☺ ⊞ ▨ ➤ ◈ ▥

S03835-3 Apistogramma sp. "ALENQUER" FEMALE
ALENQUER - DWARF-CICHLID
Alenquer/Brazil, W, 5-6cm
♀ ▷ ♬ ◑ ☺ ☺ ⊞ ▨ ➤ ◈ ▥

S03838-4 Apistogramma sp. "ALTO-NEGRO" MALE
ALTO-NEGRO - DWARF-CICHLID
Sao-Gabriel/Brazil, W, 6-7cm
♂ ▷ ♬ ◑ ☺ ☺ ⊞ ⊞ ▨ ➤ ◈ ▥

S03838-4 Apistogramma sp. "ALTO-NEGRO" FEMALE
ALTO-NEGRO - DWARF-CICHLID
Sao-Gabriel/Brazil, W, 6-7cm
♀ ▷ ♬ ◑ ☺ ☺ ⊞ ▨ ➤ ◈ ▥

S03845-3 Apistogramma sp. "BELEM" MALE
BELEM - DWARF-CICHLID
Belem/Brazil, W, 6-7cm
♂ ▷ ♬ ◑ ☺ ☺ ⊞ ▨ ➤ ◈ ▥

S03857-3 Apistogramma sp. "FELSEN/ROCK" MALE
ROCK - DWARF-CICHLID
Brazil, W, 6-7cm
♂ ▷ ♬ ◑ ☺ ☺ ⊞ ▨ ➤ ◈ ▥

APISTOGRAMMA SP. "BREITBINDEN" MALE

APISTOGRAMMA SP. "BREITBINDEN" FEMALE with babies !

© **A.C.S. Glaser GmbH**

S03848-4 Apistogramma sp. "BREITBINDEN/BROAD-STRING"
BREITBINDEN - DWARF-CICHLID   MALE
Orinoco-Area, W, 4-6cm

S03848-4 Apistogramma sp. "BREITBINDEN/BROAD-STRING"
BREITBINDEN - DWARF-CICHLID   FEMALE with babies !
Orinoco-Area, W, 4-6cm

S03850-4 Apistogramma sp. "BREITBINDEN/BROAD-STRING"
BREITBINDEN - DWARF-CICHLID   MALE
Rio-Iniridae, W, 4-6cm

S03850-4 Apistogramma sp. "BREITBINDEN/BROAD-STRING"
BREITBINDEN - DWARF-CICHLID   FEMALE
Rio-Iniridae, W, 4-6cm

S03855-3 Apistogramma sp. "CHAO" MALE
CHAO - DWARF-CICHLID
Rio-Tapajos, W, 4-5cm

S03855-3 Apistogramma sp. "CHAO" FEMALE
CHAO - DWARF-CICHLID
Rio-Tapajos, W, 4-5cm

S03860-4 Apistogramma sp. "FOUR-STRIPES" MALE
FOUR-STRIPES - DWARF-CICHLID WILD-FORM
Grenzbereich/limit-region Brazil/Venezuela, W, 6-8cm

S03860-4 Apistogramma sp. "FOUR-STRIPES" FEMALE
FOUR-STRIPES - DWARF-CICHLID WILD-FORM
Grenzbereich/limit-region Brazil/Venezuela, W, 6-8cm

S03862-3 Apistogramma sp. "FOUR-STRIPES / AGACUCHO"
AGACUCHO - DWARF-CICHLID   MALE
Puerto-Agacucho W, 6-7cm

♂ ▷ ♫ ◑ ☺ ☹ ⊞ 🖼 ➶ ◈ 🅜

S03862-3 Apistogramma sp. "FOUR-STRIPES / AGACUCHO"
AGACUCHO - DWARF-CICHLID   FEMALE
Puerto-Agacucho W, 6-7cm

♀ ▷ ♫ ◑ ☺ ☹ ⊞ 🖼 ➶ ◈ 🅜

S03865-3 Apistogramma sp. "GABELBAND/FORKBAND" FEMALE
GABELBAND - DWARF-CICHLID
Brazil (Import from Manaus), W, 4cm

♀ ▷ ♫ ◑ ☺ ☹ ⊞ 🖼 ➶ ◈ 🅜

S03870-4 Apistogramma sp. "WANGENFLECK/GILLSPOT" MALE
WANGENFLECK - DWARF-CICHLID
Para/lower-course of Amazonas/Brazil, W, 4-5cm

♂ ▷ ♫ ◑ ☺ ☹ ⊞ 🖼 ➶ ◈ 🅜

S03870-4 Apistogramma sp. "WANGENFLECK/GILLSPOT"
WANGENFLECK - DWARF-CICHLID   FEMALE
Para/lower-course of Amazonas/Brazil, W, 4-5cm

♀ ▷ ♫ ◑ ☺ ☹ ⊞ 🖼 ➶ ◈ 🅜

S03870-4 Apistogramma sp. "WANGENFLECK/GILLSPOT"
WANGENFLECK - DWARF-CICHLI FEMALE - PORTRÄT
Para/lower-course of Amazonas/Brazil, W, 4-5cm

♀ ▷ ♫ ◑ ☺ ☹ ⊞ 🖼 ➶ ◈ 🅜

S03890-4 Apistogramma sp. "PERU" MALE
PERU - DWARF-CICHLID
Iquitos/Peru, W, 5-6cm

♂ ▷ ♫ ◑ ☺ ☹ ⊞ 🖼 ➶ ◈ 🅜

S03890-4 Apistogramma sp. "PERU" FEMALE
PERU - DWARF-CICHLID
Iquitos/Peru, W, 5-6cm

♀ ▷ ♫ ◑ ☺ ☹ ⊞ 🖼 ➶ ◈ 🅜

© A.C.S. Glaser GmbH

S03895-2 Apistogramma sp. "IGARAPE-IRA" MALE
IGARAPE-IRA - DWARF-CICHLID Foto at Biotop !
Rio-Uaupes-System/Brazil, limit to Columbia, W, 5-6cm
♂ ▷ 🏦 ◑ ☺ ☺ ⊞ 🐟 ➽ ◈ 🅜

S03895-2 Apistogramma sp. "IGARAPE-IRA" FEMALE
IGARAPE-IRA - DWARF-CICHLID Foto at Biotop !
Rio-Uaupes-System/Brazil, limit to Columbia, W, 5-6cm
♀ ▷ 🏦 ◑ ☺ ☺ ⊞ 🐟 ➽ ◈ 🅜

S03900-3 Apistogramma sp. "LAGUA-ABUNA" MALE
LAGUA-ABUNA - DWARF-CICHLID
Lagua-Abuna, W, 4-5cm
♂ ▷ 🏦 ◑ ☺ ☺ ⊞ 🐟 ➽ ◈ 🅜

S03900-3 Apistogramma sp. "LAGUA-ABUNA" FEMALE
LAGUA-ABUNA - DWARF-CICHLID
Lagua Abuna, W, 4-5cm
♀ ▷ 🏦 ◑ ☺ ☺ ⊞ 🐟 ➽ ◈ 🅜

S03905-3 Apistogramma sp. "OPAL" MALE
OPAL - DWARF-CICHLID BREEDING-FORM !
Peru, B, 5-6cm
♂ ▷ 🏦 ◑ ☺ ☺ ⊞ 🐟 ➽ ◈ 🅜

S03905-3 Apistogramma sp. "OPAL" FEMALE
OPAL - DWARF-CICHLID BREEDING-FORM !
Peru, B, 5-6cm
♀ ▷ 🏦 ◑ ☺ ☺ ⊞ 🐟 ➽ ◈ 🅜

S03915-3 Apistogramma sp. "PIMENTAL"
PIMENTAL - DWARF-CICHLID
Rio-Pimental, W, 5-6cm
▷ 🏦 ◑ ☺ ☺ ⊞ 🐟 ➽ ◈ 🅜

S03925-4 Apistogramma sp. "PUERTO-NARINO" MALE
PUERTO-NARINO - DWARF similar to A. sp. REDSPOT !
UPPER-COURSE OF Amazonas near Leticia, W, 6-8cm
♂ ▷ 🏦 ◑ ☺ ☺ ⊞ 🐟 ➽ ◈ 🅜

APISTOGRAMMA SP. " RED-SPOT - BLACKSEAM"

© A.C.S. Glaser GmbH

1. Corydoras maculifer
2. Corydoras axelrodi

Diese und alle anderen demnächst in
These and all other coming soon in

Aqua**l**og "all- corydoras"

reference fish of the world

S03925-4 Apistogramma sp. "PUERTO-NARINO" FEMALE
PUERTO-NARINO - DWARF similar to a. sp. REDSPOT !
UPPER-COURSE OF Amazonas near Leticia, W, 6-8cm
♀ ▷ ♫ ◑ ☺ ☺ 💠 🖼 🐟 ◈ 🅜

S03955-3 Apistogramma sp. "REDSPOT-BLACKSEAM" MALE
REDSPOT-BLACKSEAM - DWARF-CIHCLID
Orinoco-Area/Venezuela+Columbia, W, 7-8cm
♂ ▷ ♫ ◑ ☺ ☺ 💠 🖼 🐟 ◈ 🅜

S03955-3 Apistogramma sp. "REDSPOT-BLACKSEAM" MALE
REDSPOT-BLACKSEAM - DWARF-CIchlid YOUNG
Orinoco-Area/Venezuela+Columbia, W, 7-8cm
♂ ▷ ♫ ◑ ☺ ☺ 💠 🖼 🐟 ◈ 🅜

S03956-4 Apistogramma sp. "REDSPOT" Pair
REDSPOT - DWARF-CIchlid
Orinoco-Area/Venezuela+Columbia, W, 7-8cm
♂ ♀ ▷ ♫ ◑ ☺ ☺ 💠 🖼 🐟 ◈ 🅜

S03935-3 Apistogramma sp. "RED-POINT I" MALE
REDPOINT I - DWARF-CICHLID
Florencia, Rio-Caqueta/Columbia, W, 7-8cm
♂ ▷ ♫ ◑ ☺ ☺ 💠 🖼 🐟 ◈ 🅜

S03935-3 Apistogramma sp. "RED-POINT I" FEMALE
REDPOINT I - DWARF-CICHLID
Florencia, Rio-Caqueta/Columbia, W, 7-8cm
♀ ▷ ♫ ◑ ☺ ☺ 💠 🖼 🐟 ◈ 🅜

S03940-4 Apistogramma sp. "RED-POINT II" MALE
REDPOINT II - DWARF-CICHLID
Florencia, Rio-Caqueta/Columbia, W, 7-8cm
♂ ▷ ♫ ◑ ☺ ☺ 💠 🖼 🐟 ◈ 🅜

S03940-4 Apistogramma sp. "RED-POINT II" MALE
REDPOINT II - DWARF-CICHLID PORTRÄT
Florencia, Rio-Caqueta/Columbia, W, 7-8cm
♂ ▷ ♫ ◑ ☺ ☺ 💠 🖼 🐟 ◈ 🅜

© A.C.S. Glaser GmbH

S03960-4 Apistogramma sp. "ROTKEIL / RED-WEDGE" MALE
ROTKEIL - DWARF-CICHLID (same as Ap. uaupesi !)
Rio-UaupesBrazil, W, 7-8cm

♂ ▷ ♫ ◑ ☺ ☺ ⊞ 🖼 ➡ ◈ m

S03960-4 Apistogramma sp. "ROTKEIL / RED-WEDGE" FEMALE
ROTKEIL - DWARF-CICHLID (same as Ap. uaupesi !)
Rio-Uaupes/Brazil, W, 7-8cm

♀ ▷ ♫ ◑ ☺ ☺ ⊞ 🖼 ➡ ◈ m

S03960-4 Apistogramma sp. "ROTKEIL / RED-WEDGE" MALE
ROTKEIL - DWARF-CICHLID (same as Ap. uaupesi !)
Rio-Uaupes/Brazil, W, 7-8cm

♂ ▷ ♫ ◑ ☺ ☺ ⊞ 🖼 ➡ ◈ m

S03965-3 Apistogramma sp. "RIO-BRANCO" MALE
BRANCO - DWARF-CICHLID
Rio-Branco, W, 5-6cm

♂ ▷ ♫ ◑ ☺ ☺ ⊞ 🖼 ➡ ◈ m

S03970-4 Apistogramma sp. "RIO-CAURA" MALE
CAURA - DWARF-CICHLID
Rio- Caura, W, 5-6cm

♂ ▷ ♫ ◑ ☺ ☺ ⊞ 🖼 ➡ ◈ m

S03975-3 Apistogramma sp. "RIO-PEIXOTO" MALE
PEIXOTO - DWARF-CICHLID
Rio Teles-Pires - Area/Brazil, W, 5-6cm

♂ ▷ ♫ ◑ ☺ ☺ ⊞ 🖼 ➡ ◈ m

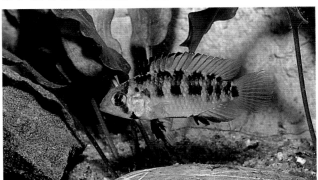

S03975-3 Apistogramma sp. "RIO-PEIXOTO" MALE
PEIXOTO - DWARF-CICHLID
Rio Teles-Pires - Area/Brazil, W, 5-6cm

♂ ▷ ♫ ◑ ☺ ☺ ⊞ 🖼 ➡ ◈ m

S03975-3 Apistogramma sp. "RIO-PEIXOTO" MALE
PEIXOTO - DWARF-CICHLID
Rio Teles-Pires - Area/Brazil, W, 5-6cm

♂ ▷ ♫ ◑ ☺ ☺ ⊞ 🖼 ➡ ◈ m

S03980-3 Apistogramma sp. "RIO-VAUPES" MALE
RIO-VAUPES - DWARF-CICHLID
Mitu, Rio-Vaupes/Columbia, W, 5-6cm

S03980-3 Apistogramma sp. "RIO-VAUPES" FEMALE
RIO-VAUPES - DWARF-CICHLID
Mitu, Rio-Vaupes/Columbia, W, 5-6cm

S03990-3 Apistogramma sp. "RED-STROKE"
RED-STROKE - DWARF similar Ap. hongsloi !
Orinoco/Venezuela, W, Male 8cm + Female 5cm

S03995-4 Apistogramma sp. "SEGELFLOSSER / SAILFIN" MALE
SAILFIN - DWARF-CICHLID
Rio Negro-area/Columbia, W, Male 8cm + Female 6cm

S04005-2 Apistogramma sp. "SMARAGD" Polygamy: only this sp.
SMARAGD - DWARF-CICHLID   is living 1 Female togeth.
Santarem/Brazil, W, 6cm   with many Male !

S04005-2 Apistogr.sp."SMARAGD" MALE Polygamy: only this spec.
SMARAGD - DWARF-CICHLID   is living 1 Female togeth.
Santarem/Brazil, W, 6cm   with many Male !

S04005-3 A. sp."SMARAGD" MALE Polygamy: only this spec.
SMARAGD - DWARF-CICHLID   is living 1 Female togeth.
Santarem/Brazil, W, 6cm   with many Male !

S04005-3 A. sp."SMARAGD" PAIR Polygamy: only this spec.
SMARAGD - DWARF-CICHLID   is living 1 Female togeth.
Santarem/Brazil, W, 6cm   with many Male !

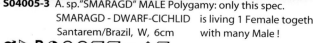

© **A.C.S. Glaser GmbH**

APISTOGRAMMA TRIFASCIATA   MALE

APISTOGRAMMOIDES PUCALLPAENSIS   MALE

S04010-3 Apistogramma sp. "TIQUIE I"
TIQUIE I - DWARF-CICHLID
Rio-Tiquie,limit-region Brazil/Columbia, W, 4cm

S04015-4 Apistogramma sp. "TUCURUI" MALE
TUCURUI - DWARF-CICHLID
Rio-Tapajos, Tucurui-dam, W, 5-6cm

S04015-4 Apistogramma sp. "TUCURUI" MALE
TUCURUI - DWARF-CICHLID
Rio-Tapajos, Tucurui-dam, W, 5-6cm

S04015-4 Apistogramma sp. "TUCURUI" FEMALE
TUCURUI - DWARF-CICHLID
Rio-Tapajos, Tucurui-dam, W, 5-6cm

S04015-4 Apistogramma sp. "TUCURUI" FEMALE
TUCURUI - DWARF-CICHLID
Rio-Tapajos, Tucurui-dam, W, 5-6cm

S04030-3 Apistogramma sp. "GELBWANGEN / YELLOW-CHEEK"
GELBWANGEN - DWARF-CICHLID   MALE
lower-course Rio-Negro, Manaus-Area/Brazil, W, 6-7cm

S04045-4 Apistogramma staecki MALE
CROSSWAYS - DWARF-CICHLID
North of Bolivia, Trinidad-area, Male 5cm + Female 3cm

S04250-3 Apistogramma steindachneri (= wickleri+ornatipinnis)
STEINDACHNER - DWARF-CICHLID   MALE
Guayana-Countries, W, Male 10cm + Female 7cm

© A.C.S. Glaser GmbH

S04250-3 Apistogramma steindachneri (= .wickleri+ornatipinnis)
STEINDACHNER - DWARF-CICHLID   PAIR
Guayana-Countries, W, Male 10cm + Female 7cm
♂ ♀ ▷ 🦂 ◐ ☺ ☺ 🗊 🖼 ➥ ◈ m̄

S04250-4 Apistogramma steindachneri (= .wickleri+ornatipinnis)
STEINDACHNER - DWARF-CICHLID   MALE
Guayana-Countries, W, Male 10cm + Female 7cm
♂ ▷ 🦂 ◐ ☺ ☺ 🗊 🖼 ➥ ◈ m̄

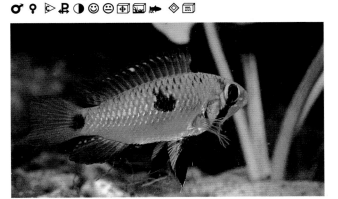

S04250-4 Apistogramma steindachneri (= wickleri+ornatipinnis)
STEINDACHNER - DWARF-CICHLID   FEMALE
Guayana-Countries, W, Male 10cm + Female 7cm
♀ ▷ 🦂 ◐ ☺ ☺ 🗊 🖼 ➥ ◈ m̄

S04250-4 Apistogramma steindachneri (= wickleri+ornatipinnis)
STEINDACHNER - DWARF-CICHLID   MALE
Guayana-Countries, W, Male 10cm + Female 7cm
♂ ▷ 🦂 ◐ ☺ ☺ 🗊 🖼 ➥ ◈ m̄

S04270-3 Apistogramma taeniata   MALE
TAENIA - DWARF-CICHLID
Rio-Cupari, W, 6-7cm
♂ ▷ 🦂 ◐ ☺ ☺ 🗊 🖼 ➥ ◈ m̄

S04270-3 Apistogramma taeniata   FEMALE at brood-nurse
TAENIA - DWARF-CICHLID
Rio-Cupari, W, 6-7cm
♀ ▷ 🦂 ◐ ☺ ☺ 🗊 🖼 ➥ ◈ m̄

S04270-3 Apistogramma taeniata   MALE
TAENIA - DWARF-CICHLID
Rio-Cupari, B, 6-7cm
♂ ▷ 🦂 ◐ ☺ ☺ 🗊 🖼 ➥ ◈ m̄

S04270-3 Apistogramma taeniata   FEMALE
TAENIA - DWARF-CICHLID
Rio-Cupari, B, 6-7cm
♀ ▷ 🦂 ◐ ☺ ☺ 🗊 🖼 ➥ ◈ m̄

S04273-4 Apistogramma taeniata   Typart-Apistogramma !
TAENIA - DWARF-CICHLID
Rio-Cupari, B, 6-7cm

S04280-2 Apistogramma sp. taeniata
TAENIA - DWARF-CICHLID
Rio-Cupari, B, 5-6cm

S04290-3 Apistogramma taeniata "RUROPOLIS"   MALE
RURPOLIS - DWARF-CICHLID
Rio-Rurupolis/Tapajos/Brazil, W, 5-6cm

S04290-3 Apistogramma taeniata "RUROPOLIS"   FEMALE
RURPOLIS - DWARF-CICHLID
Rio-Rurupolis/Tapajos/Brazil, W, 5-6cm

S04295-3 Apistogramma taeniata "SANTAREM" MALE
SANTAREM - DWARF-CICHLID
Santarem/Rio-Tapajos/Brazil, W, 5-6cm

S04295-3 Apistogramma taeniata "SANTAREM" FEMALE
SANTAREM - DWARF-CICHLID
Santarem/Rio-Tapajos/Brazil, W, 5-6cm

S04320-2 Apistogramma trifasciata MALE Juvenil
TRIFASCIATA - DWARF-CICHLID "BREEDING-FORM"
Rio-Paraguaya/Rio-Guapore, B, Male 6cm + Fem.4-5cm

S04320-2 Apistogramma trifasciata PAIR Juvenil
TRIFASCIATA - DWARF-CICHLID "BREEDING-FORM"
Rio-Paraguaya/Rio-Guapore, B, Male 6cm + Fem.4-5cm

© A.C.S. Glaser GmbH

S04320-4 Apistogramma trifasciata MALE
TRIFASCIATA - DWARF-CICHLID "BREEDING-FORM"
Rio-Paraguaya/Rio-Guapore, B, Male 6cm + Fem.4-5cm

S04320-4 Apistogramma trifasciata FEMALE
TRIFASCIATA - DWARF-CICHLID "BREEDING-FORM"
Rio-Paraguaya/Rio-Guapore, B, Male 6cm-Fem.4-5cm

S04015-2 Apistogramma sp. "TUCURUI"
TUCURUI - DWARF-CICHLID
Rio-Tapajos, Tucurui-dam, W, 5-6cm

S04015-2 Apistogramma sp. "TUCURUI"
TUCURUI - DWARF-CICHLID
Rio-Tapajos, Tucurui-dam, W, 5-6cm

S04360-3 Apistogramma uaupesi "RIO-UAUPESI" MALE
UAUPES - DWARF-CICHLID (same as Ap.sp.ROTKEIL !)
Rio Uaupes-Area, W, 4-5cm

S04360-3 Apistogramma uaupesi "RIO-UAUPESI" FEMALE
UAUPES - DWARF-CICHLID (same as A.sp.ROTKEIL !)
Rio Uaupes-Area, W, 4-5cm

S04365-2 Apistogramma cf. uaupesi "RIO-UAUPESI" MALE
UAUPES - DWARF-CICHLID
Rio-Atabapo, W, 5-6cm

S04370-3 Apistogramma uaupesi "UNEIUXI" MALE
UNEIUXI - DWARF-CICHLID (before A.sp.ROTKEIL !?)
Rio-Uneiuxi, W, 5-6cm

DICROSSUS (before Crenicara !) FILAMENTOSUS MALE

© A.C.S. Glaser GmbH

DICROSSUS (before Crenicara !) MACULATUS MALE

S04380-3 Apistogramma uaupesi "URUBAXI" MALE
UAUPES - DWARF-CICHLID (befor Ap.sp.ROTKEIL !)
Rio-Urubaxi, W, 5-6cm
♂ ▷ ♫ ◑ ☺ ☺ ⊞ ▦ ➤ ◈ 🔳

S04400-3 Apistogramma urteagai MALE
URTEAGAI - DWARF-CICHLID
Peru + Bolivia, W, 5-6cm
♂ ▷ ♫ ◑ ☺ ☺ ⊞ ▦ ➤ ◈ 🔳

S04400-3 Apistogramma urteagai FEMALE
URTEAGAI - DWARF-CICHLID
Peru + Bolivia, W, 5-6cm
♀ ▷ ♫ ◑ ☺ ☺ ⊞ ▦ ➤ ◈ 🔳

S04430-4 Apistogramma viejita MALE
VIEJITA - DWARF-CICHLID
Puerto Gaitan/Columbia, W, Male 7-8cm + Fem. 4cm
♂ ▷ ♫ ◑ ☺ ☺ ⊞ ▦ ➤ ◈ 🔳

S04440-4 Apistogramma viejita "RIO-META" MALE
META-VIEJITA - DWARF-CICHLID
Rio-Meta/Columbia, W, Male 7-8cm + Fem. 4cm
♂ ▷ ♫ ◑ ☺ ☺ ⊞ ▦ ➤ ◈ 🔳

S04440-4 Apistogramma viejita "RIO-META" FEMALE
META-VIEJITA - DWARF-CICHLID
Rio-Meta/Columbia, W, Male 7-8cm + Fem. 4cm
♀ ▷ ♫ ◑ ☺ ☺ ⊞ ▦ ➤ ◈ 🔳

S04450-5 Apistogramma viejita II MALE
VIEJITA II - DWARF-CICHLID
Rio-Meta/Columbia, B, Male 7-8cm + Fem. 4cm
♂ ▷ ♫ ◑ ☺ ☺ ⊞ ▦ ➤ ◈ 🔳

S04450-5 Apistogramma viejita II FEMALE
VIEJITA II - DWARF-CICHLID
Rio-Meta/Columbia, B, Male 7-8cm + Fem. 4cm
♀ ▷ ♫ ◑ ☺ ☺ ⊞ ▦ ➤ ◈ 🔳

© **A.C.S. Glaser GmbH**

S04500-2 Apistogrammoides pucallpaensis MALE
PUCALLPA - DWARF-CICHLID
Amazonas-Area/Peru, W, Male 4-5cm + Female 3cm

♂ ▷ ⌶ ◑ ☺ ☻ ⊞ ▤ ➤ ◈ ▥

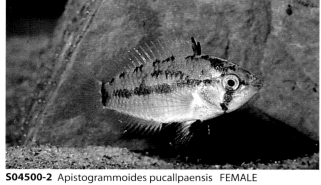

S04500-2 Apistogrammoides pucallpaensis FEMALE
PUCALLPA - DWARF-CICHLID
Amazonas-Area/Peru, W, Male 4-5cm + Female 3cm

♀ ▷ ⌶ ◑ ☺ ☻ ⊞ ▤ ➤ ◈ ▥

S04500-3 Apistogrammoides pucallpaensis MALE
PUCALLPA - DWARF-CICHLID
Amazonas-Area/Peru, W, Male 4-5cm + Female 3cm

♂ ▷ ⌶ ◑ ☺ ☻ ⊞ ▤ ➤ ◈ ▥

S04500-3 Apistogrammoides pucallpaensis FEMALE
PUCALLPA - DWARF-CICHLID
Amazonas-Area/Peru, W, Male 4-5cm + Female 3cm

♀ ▷ ⌶ ◑ ☺ ☻ ⊞ ▤ ➤ ◈ ▥

S045004 Apistogrammoides pucallpaensis MALE
PUCALLPA - DWARF-CICHLID BREEDING-FORM
Amazonas-Area/Peru, B, Male 4-5cm + Female 3cm

♂ ▷ ⌶ ◑ ☺ ☻ ⊞ ▤ ➤ ◈ ▥

S045004 Apistogrammoides pucallpaensis FEMALE
PUCALLPA - DWARF-CICHLID BREEDING-FORM
Amazonas-Area/Peru, B, Male 4-5cm + Female 3cm

♀ ▷ ⌶ ◑ ☺ ☻ ⊞ ▤ ➤ ◈ ▥

S04500-4 Apistogrammoides pucallpaensis MALE
PUCALLPA - DWARF-CICHLID BREEDING-FORM
Amazonas-Area/Peru, B, Male 4-5cm + Female 3cm

♂ ▷ ⌶ ◑ ☺ ☻ ⊞ ▤ ➤ ◈ ▥

S04500-4 Apistogrammoides pucallpaensis FEMALE
PUCALLPA - DWARF-CICHLID BREEDING-FORM
Amazonas-Area/Peru, B, Male 4-5cm + Female 3cm

♀ ▷ ⌶ ◑ ☺ ☻ ⊞ ▤ ➤ ◈ ▥

S04500-4 Apistogrammoides pucallpaensis MALE
PUCALLPA - DWARF-CICHLID BREEDING-FORM
Amazonas-Area/Peru, B, Male 4-5cm + Female 3cm

♂ ▷ ♫ ◐ ☺ ☹ ⊞ 🖼 ➟ ◈ 🔲

S04500-4 Apistogrammoides pucallpaensis FEMALE
PUCALLPA - DWARF-CICHLID BREEDING-FORM
Amazonas-Area/Peru, B, Male 4-5cm + Female 3cm

♀ ▷ ♫ ◐ ☺ ☹ ⊞ 🖼 ➟ ◈ 🔲

S07320-3 Biotoecus opercularis
BIOTOECUS
Lake-Saraca, W, 8-10cm

▷ ♫ ◐ ☹ ⊞ 🖼 ➟ ⚠ 🔲

S07320-3 Biotoecus opercularis
BIOTOECUS
Lake-Saraca, W, 8-10cm

▷ ♫ ◐ ☹ ⊞ 🖼 ➟ ⚠ 🔲

S22815-3 Crenicara latruncularium
LATRUN - CRENICARA
Brazil, W, 7-9cm

▷ ⫸P ◐ ☺ ☹ ⊞ 🖼 ➟ ◈ ⚠ 🔲

S22815-2 Crenicara latruncularium
LATRUN - CRENICARA
Brazil, W, 7-9cm

♂ ▷ ♫ ◐ ☺ ⊞ 🖼 ➟ ◈ 🔲

S22820-3 Crenicara punctulata MALE
PUNCTU - CRENICARA
Peru, W, Male 10-12cm + Female 7-8cm

♂ ▷ ♫ ◐ ☺ ⊞ 🖼 ➟ ◈ 🔲

S22820-3 Crenicara punctulata FEMALE
PUNCTU - CRENICARA
Peru, W, Male 10-12cm + Female 7-8cm

♀ ▷ ♫ ◐ ☺ ⊞ 🖼 ➟ ◈ 🔲

© A.C.S. Glaser GmbH

MICROGEOPHAGUS (before Papiliochromis !) altispinosus

Biotop in Southamerica / Luftaufnahme von RIO MARIE / AERIAL - PHOTOGRAPH of RIO-MARIE

© **A.C.S. Glaser GmbH**

S22820-3 Crenicara punctulata MALE
PUNCTU - CRENICARA
Amazonas-Area/Brazil, W, Male 10-12cm + Fem.7-8cm

S22820-3 Crenicara punctulata FEMALE
PUNCTU - CRENICARA
Amazonas-Area/Brazil, W, Male 10-12cm + Fem.7-8cm

S22830-3 Crenicara punctulata "GUAYANA" MALE
PUNCTU - CRENICARA
Br.-Guayana, W, 8-9cm

S22830-3 Crenicara punctulata "GUAYANA" FEMALE
PUNCTU - CRENICARA
Br.-Guayana, W, 8-9cm

S31160-3 Dicrossus filamentosus MALE
CHECKERBOARD (all Dicrossus before Crenicara !)
Rio Negro-Area/Brazil, W, Male 7-8cm + Female 6cm

S31160-3 Dicrossus filamentosus FEMALE
CHECKERBOARD (all Dicrossus before Crenicara !)
Rio Negro-Area/Brazil, W, Male 7-8cm + Female 6cm

S31160-4 Dicrossus filamentosus MALE
CHECKERBOARD (all Dicrossus before Crenicara !)
Rio Negro-Area/Brazil, W, Male 7-8cm + Female 6cm

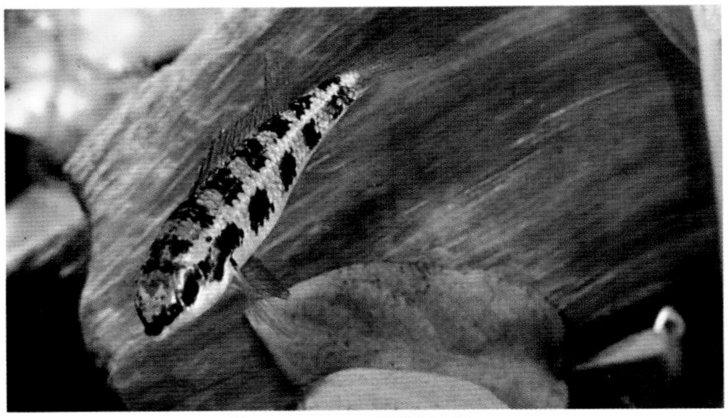

S31160-4 Dicrossus filamentosus FEMALE
CHECKERBOARD (all Dicrossus befor e Crenicara !)
Rio Negro-Area/Brazil, W, Male 7-8cm + Female 6cm

S31160-4 Dicrossus filamentosus FEMALE colour at spawn!
CHECKERBOARD (all Dicrossus before Crenicara !)
Rio Negro-Area/Brazil, W, Male 7-8cm + Female 6cm

♀ ▷ ⵏP ◐ ☺ ☺ 🖽 🖼 ➡ ◈ ⚠ 🔲

S31160-4 Dicrossus filamentosus   PAIR
CHECKERBOARD (all Dicrossus before Crenicara !)
Rio Negro-Area/Brazil, W, Male 7-8cm + Female 6cm

♂ ♀ ▷ ⵏP ◐ ☺ ☺ 🖽 🖼 ➡ ◈ ⚠ 🔲

S31185-2 Dicrossus maculatus Male semiadult !
MACULATA (all Dicrossus before Crenicara !)
Amazonas-Area/Tocantins, Male 6-7cm + Fem.4cm

♂ ▷ ⵏP ◐ ☺ ☺ 🖽 🖼 ➡ ◈ ⚠ 🔲

S31185-4 Dicrossus maculatus Male adult !
MACULATA (all Dicrossus before Crenicara !)
Amazonas-Area/Tocantins, Male 6-7cm + Fem.4cm

♂ ▷ ⵏP ◐ ☺ ☺ 🖽 🖼 ➡ ◈ ⚠ 🔲

S31185-3 Dicrossus maculatus FEMALE
MACULATA (all Dicrossus before Crenicara !)
Amazonas-Area/Tocantins, Male 6-7cm + Fem.4cm

♀ ▷ ⵏP ◐ ☺ ☺ 🖽 🖼 ➡ ◈ ⚠ 🔲

S31186-4 Dicrossus maculatus Male BREEDING-FORM
MACULATA (all Dicrossus before Crenicara !)
Amazonas-Area/Tocantins, B, Male 6-7cm + Fem.4cm

♂ ▷ ₿ ◐ ☺ 🖽 🖼 ➡ ◈ 🔲

S31186-4 Dicrossus maculatus FEMALE BREEDING-FORM
MACULATA (all Dicrossus before Crenicara !)
Amazonas-Area/Tocantins, B, Male 6-7cm + Fem.4cm

♀ ▷ ₿ ◐ ☺ 🖽 🖼 ➡ ◈ 🔲

S31186-4 Dicrossus maculatus PAIR BREEDING-FORM
MACULATA (all Dicrossus before Crenicara !)
Amazonas-Area/Tocantins, B, Male 6-7cm + Fem.4cm

♂ ♀ ▷ ₿ ◐ ☺ 🖽 🖼 ➡ ◈ 🔲

© A.C.S. Glaser GmbH

S31195-4 Dicrossus sp. "DOUBLE-SPOT"
DOUBLE-SPOT-CRENIC. (all Dicrossus before Crenicara !)
Rio-Javari, W, Male 6-7cm + Fem.4cm

S31198-3 Dicrossus sp. "TAPAJOS" MALE
TAPAJOS - CRENIC. (all Dicrossus before Crenicara !)
Rio-Tapajos, North-Brazil, W, Male 6-7cm + Fem.4cm

S31198-3 Dicrossus sp. "TAPAJOS" FEMALE
TAPAJOS - CRENIC. (all Dicrossus before Crenicara !)
Rio-Tapajos, North-Brazil, W, Male 6-7cm + Fem.4cm

S31197-4 Dicrossus sp. "TAPAJOS" FEMALE BREEDING-COLOUR
TAPAJOS - CRENIC. (all Dicrossus before Crenicara !)
Rio-Tapajos, North-Brazil, W, Male 6-7cm + Fem.4cm

S31196-3 Dicrossus sp. "RIO-NEGRO" MALE
NEGRO - CRENIC. (all Dicrossus before Crenicara !)
Rio-Negro/North-Brazil, W, 6-8cm

S31196-3 Dicrossus sp. "RIO-NEGRO" FEMALE
NEGRO - CRENIC. (all Dicrossus befor e Crenicara !)
Rio-Negro/North-Brazil, W, 6-8cm

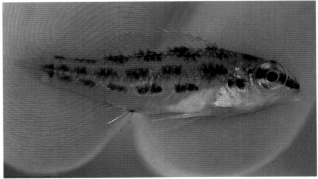

S31199-4 Dicrossus sp. "ITAITUBA"
ITAITUBA - CRENIC. (all Dicrossus befor e Crenicara !)
Itaituba/Tapajos/Brazil, W, 6-7cm

Herotilapia multispinosa / RAINBOW - CICHLID
Der, und alle anderen demnächst / all other coming soon
in "SOUTHAMERICAN - CICHLIDS III"

S52005-2 Microgeophagus altispinosus
ALTISPINOSA-BUTTERFLY Rio-Mamore/Bolivia
(all Microgeophagus beforePapiliochromis!) W, 7-8cm
▷ ♫ ◐ ☺ ☻ ⊞ 🖼 ➤ ◈ 🔟

S52005-2 Microgeophagus altispinosus
ALTISPINOSA-BUTTERFLY Rio-Mamore/Bolivia
(all Microgeophagus before Papiliochromis!) W, 7-8cm
▷ ♫ ◐ ☺ ☻ ⊞ 🖼 ➤ ◈ 🔟

S52005-3 Microgeophagus altispinosus MALE
ALTISPINOSA-BUTTERFLY Rio-Mamore/Bolivia
(all Microgeophagus before Papiliochromis!) W, 7-8cm
♂ ▷ ♫ ◐ ☺ ☻ ⊞ 🖼 ➤ ◈ 🔟

S52005-3 Microgeophagus altispinosus FEMALE
ALTISPINOSA-BUTTERFLY Rio-Mamore/Bolivia
(all Microgeophagus before Papiliochromis!) W, 7-8cm
♀ ▷ ♫ ◐ ☺ ☻ ⊞ 🖼 ➤ ◈ 🔟

S52015-4 Microgeophagus altispinosus "MATO-GROSSO"
ALTISPINOSA-BUTTERFLY Mato-Grosso/Brazil
(all Microgeophagus before Papiliochromis!) W, 7-8cm
▷ ♫ ◐ ☺ ☻ ⊞ 🖼 ➤ ◈ 🔟

S52005-4 Microgeophagus altispinosus
ALTISPINOSA-BUTTERFLY Rio-Mamore/Bolivia
(all Microgeophagus before Papiliochromis!) W, 7-8cm
▷ ♫ ◐ ☺ ☻ ⊞ 🖼 ➤ ◈ 🔟

S52005-4 Microgeophagus altispinosus
ALTISPINOSA-BUTTERFLY Rio-Mamore/Bolivia
(all Microgeophagus before Papiliochromis!) W, 7-8cm
▷ ♫ ◐ ☺ ☻ ⊞ 🖼 ➤ ◈ 🔟

S52005-4 Microgeophagus altispinosus
ALTISPINOSA-BUTTERFLY Rio-Mamore/Bolivia
(all Microgeophagus before Papiliochromis!) W, 7-8cm
▷ ♫ ◐ ☺ ☻ ⊞ 🖼 ➤ ◈ 🔟

© **A.C.S. Glaser GmbH**

S52005-2 Microgeophagus altispinosus JUVENIL-Schwarm/school
ALTISPINOSA-BUTTERFLY   Rio-Mamore/Bolivia
(all Microgeophagus before Papiliochromis!)   W, 7-8cm
▷♫◑☺☻⊞🖼️🐌 ◈🔲

S52006-4 Microgeophagus altispinosus MALE BREEDING-FORM
ALTISPINOSA-BUTTERFLY   Rio-Mamore/Bolivia
(all Microgeophagus before Papiliochromis!)   B, 7-8cm
♂▷♫◑☺⊞🖼️🐌 ◈🔲

S52006-4 Microgeophagus altispinosus MALE BREEDING-FORM
ALTISPINOSA-BUTTERFLY   Rio-Mamore/Bolivia
(all Microgeophagus before Papiliochromis!)   B, 7-8cm
♂▷♫◑☺⊞🖼️🐌 ◈🔲

S52006-4 Microgeophagus altispinosus PAIR BREEDING-FORM
ALTISPINOSA-BUTTERFLY   Rio-Mamore/Bolivia
(all Microgeophagus before Papiliochromis!)   B, 7-8cm
♂♀▷♫◑☺⊞🖼️🐌 ◈🔲

S52006-4 Microgeophagus altispinosus PAIR at pairing !
ALTISPINOSA-BUTTERFLY   Rio-Mamore/Bolivia
(all Microgeophagus before Papiliochromis!)   B, 7-8cm
♂♀▷♫◑☺⊞🖼️🐌 ◈🔲

S52006-4 Microgeophagus altispinosus PAIR with spawn !
ALTISPINOSA-BUTTERFLY   Rio-Mamore/Bolivia
(all Microgeophagus before Papiliochromis!)   B, 7-8cm
♂♀▷♫◑☺⊞🖼️🐌 ◈🔲

S52006-4 Microgeophagus altispinosus PAIR with larves !
ALTISPINOSA-BUTTERFLY   Rio-Mamore/Bolivia
(all Microgeophagus before Papiliochromis!)   B, 7-8cm
♂♀▷♫◑☺⊞🖼️🐌 ◈🔲

S52006-4 Microgeophagus altispinosus PAIR with babies !
ALTISPINOSA-BUTTERFLY   Rio-Mamore/Bolivia
(all Microgeophagus before Papiliochromis!)   B, 7-8cm
♂♀▷♫◑☺⊞🖼️🐌 ◈🔲

S52013-4 Microgeophagus altispinosus DOUBLE-SPOT-FORM
ALTISPINOSA-BUTTERFLY   Rio-Mamore/Bolivia
(all Microgeophagus before Papiliochromis!)   W, 7-8cm

S52017-4 Microgeophagus cf. altispinosus
ALTISPINOSA-BUTTERFLY
(all Microgeophagus before Papiliochromis!)   Bolivia, W, 7cm

S52020-3 Microgeophagus ramirezi
BUTTERFLY - DWARF-CICHLID   Venezuela + Columbia
(all Microgeophagus before Papiliochromis!)   W, 6-7cm

S52020-3 Microgeophagus ramirezi
BUTTERFLY - DWARF-CICHLID   Venezuela + Columbia
(all Microgeophagus before Papiliochromis!)   W, 6-7cm

S52020-4 Microgeophagus ramirezi MALE
BUTTERFLY - DWARF-CICHLID   Venezuela + Columbia
(all Microgeophagus before Papiliochromis!)   W, 6-7cm

S52020-4 Microgeophagus ramirezi FEMALE
BUTTERFLY - DWARF-CICHLID   Venezuela + Columbia
(all Microgeophagus before Papiliochromis!)   W, 6-7cm

S52021-4 Microgeophagus ramirezi   MALE
BUTTERFLY - DWARF-CICHLID   Orinoco/Venezuela
(all Microgeophagus before Papiliochromis!)   W, 5-6cm

S52021-4 Microgeophagus ramirezi   FEMALE
BUTTERFLY - DWARF-CICHLID   Orinoco/Venezuela
(all Microgeophagus before Papiliochromis!)   W, 5-6cm

© A.C.S. Glaser GmbH

S52020-4 Microgeophagus ramirezi PAIR mit Gelege/with eggs !
BUTTERFLY - DWARF-CICHLID   Venezuela/Columbia
(all Microgeophagus before Papiliochromis !)   B, 6-7cm

♂ ♀ ▷ ฿ ◑ ☺ ⊞ 🖼 ➠ ◈ Ⓢ

S52020-4 Microgeophagus ramirezi   MALE
BUTTERFLY - DWARF-CICHLID   Venezuela/Columbia
(all Microgeophagus before Papiliochromis !)   B, 6-7cm

♂ ▷ ฿ ◑ ☺ ⊞ 🖼 ➠ ◈ Ⓢ

S52020-4 Microgeophagus ramirezi   FEMALE
BUTTERFLY - DWARF-CICHLID   Venezuela/Columbia
(all Microgeophagus before Papiliochromis !)   B, 6-7cm

♀ ▷ ฿ ◑ ☺ ⊞ 🖼 ➠ ◈ Ⓢ

S52020-4 Microgeophagus ramirezi   PAIR
BUTTERFLY - DWARF-CICHLID   Venezuela/Columbia
(all Microgeophagus before Papiliochromis !)   B, 6-7cm

♂ ♀ ▷ ฿ ◑ ☺ ⊞ 🖼 ➠ ◈ Ⓢ

S52025-4 Microgeophagus ramirezi "ASIA-BREEDING" MALE
BUTTERFLY - DWARF-CICHLID   Venezuela/Columbia
(all Microgeophagus before Papiliochromis !)   Z, 6-7cm

♂ ▷ ฿ ◑ ☺ ⊞ 🖼 ➠ ◈ Ⓢ

S52035-2 Microgeophagus ramirezi "WHITE"
WHITE-BUTTERFLY - DWARF   Venezuela/Columbia
(all Microgeophagus before Papiliochromis !)   Z, 6-7cm

▷ ฿ ◑ ☺ ⊞ 🖼 ➠ ◈ Ⓢ

S52035-3 Microgeophagus ramirezi "WHITE"
WHITE-BUTTERFLY - DWARF   Venezuela/Columbia
(all Microgeophagus before Papiliochromis !)   Z, 6-7cm

▷ ฿ ◑ ☺ ⊞ 🖼 ➠ ◈ Ⓢ

S52036-3 Microgeophagus ramirezi "GOLD"
GOLD-BUTTERFLY - DWARF   Venezuela/Columbia
(all Microgeophagus before Papiliochromis !)   Z, 6-7cm

♂ ▷ ฿ ◑ ☺ ⊞ 🖼 ➠ ◈ Ⓢ

S52038-4 Microgeophagus ramirezi "RED-GOLD" MALE
RED-GOLD-BUTTERFLY - DWARF Venezuela/Columbia
(all Microgeophagus before Papiliochromis !) Z, 6-7cm
♂ ▷ ♬ ◑ ☺ ⊞ ▧ ➡ ◈ Ⓢ

S52038-4 Microgeophagus ramirezi "RED-GOLD" MALE
RED-GOLD-BUTTERFLY - DWARF Venezuela/Columbia
(all Microgeophagus before Papiliochromis !) Z, 6-7cm
♂ ▷ ♬ ◑ ☺ ⊞ ▧ ➡ ◈ Ⓢ

S52040-3 Microgeophagus sp. "BRAZIL" MALE
BRAZIL-BUTTERFLY - DWARF   Brazil
(all Microgeophagus before Papiliochromis !) W, 7cm
♂ ▷ ♬ ◑ ☺ ☺ ⊞ ▧ ➡ ◈ Ⓢ

S52045-3 Microgeophagus sp. "TWO-POINT"
TWO-POINT - BUTTERFLY-DWARF Columbia
(all Microgeophagus before Papiliochromis !) W, 6-7cm
▷ ♬ ◑ ☺ ☺ ⊞ ▧ ➡ ◈ Ⓢ

S53205-4 "Nannacara" hoehnei (probably Aequidens) MALE adult
HOENEI - NANNACARA mit Gelege/with eggs !
Mato-Grosso - Area/Brazil, W, 9-10cm
♂ ▷ ♬ ◑ ☺ ☺ ⊞ ▧ ➡ ◈ ⚠ ▥

S53205-4 "Nannacara" hoehnei (probably Aequidens)
HOENEI - NANNACARA WILD-FORM
Mato-Grosso - Area/Brazil, W, 9-10cm
▷ ♬ ◑ ☺ ☺ ⊞ ▧ ➡ ◈ ⚠ ▥

S53210-4 Nannacara adoketa MALE   F 1 - Nachzucht/Breeding
ADOK - NANNACARA
Rio-Negro + Uaupes/Brazil, W, Male 12cm+Female 8cm
♂ ▷ ♬ ◑ ☺ ☺ ⊞ ▧ ➡ ◈ ⚠ ▥

S53210-4 Nannacara adoketa FEMALE
ADOK - NANNACARA
Rio-Negro + Uaupes/Brazil, W, Male 12cm+Female 8cm
♀ ▷ ♬ ◑ ☺ ☺ ⊞ ▧ ➡ ◈ ⚠ ▥

© A.C.S. Glaser GmbH

S53212-4 Nannacara adoketa "RIO-UAUPES" MALE
ADOK - NANNACARA
Rio- Uaupes/Brazil, W, Male 12cm+Female 8cm
♂ ▷ ♫ ◗ ☺ ☺ ⊞ 🐟 ➤ ◈ ⚠ 🆂 Ⓜ

S53212-4 Nannacara adoketa "RIO-UAUPES" FEMALE
ADOK - NANNACARA
Rio- Uaupes/Brazil, W, Male 12cm+Female 8cm
♀ ▷ ♫ ◗ ☺ ☺ ⊞ 🐟 ➤ ◈ ⚠ 🆂 Ⓜ

S53212-4 Nannacara adoketa "RIO-UAUPES" MALE
ADOK - NANNACARA   PORTRÄT
Rio- Uaupes/Brazil, W, Male 12cm+Female 8cm
♂ ▷ ♫ ◗ ☺ ☺ ⊞ 🐟 ➤ ◈ ⚠ 🆂 Ⓜ

S53215-4 Nannacara anomala MALE
ANOMALA - NANNACARA
West-Guayana, W, Male 8cm + Female 6cm
♂ ▷ ♫ ◗ ☺ ⊞ 🐟 ➤ ◈ 🆂

S53215-4 Nannacara anomala FEMALE
ANOMALA - NANNACARA
West-Guayana, W, Male 8cm + Female 6cm
♀ ▷ ♫ ◗ ☺ ⊞ 🐟 ➤ ◈ 🆂

S53215-4 Nannacara anomala FEMALE Balzfärbung !
ANOMALA - NANNACARA   at mating-season !
West-Guayana, W, Male 8cm + Female 6cm
♀ ▷ ♫ ◗ ☺ ⊞ 🐟 ➤ ◈ 🆂

S53215-4 Nannacara anomala MALE
ANOMALA - NANNACARA
West-Guayana, B, Male 8cm + Female 6cm
♂ ▷ ♫ ◗ ☺ ⊞ 🐟 ➤ ◈ 🆂

S53215-4 Nannacara anomala FEMALE with babies !
ANOMALA - NANNACARA
West-Guayana, B, Male 8cm + Female 6cm
♀ ▷ ♫ ◗ ☺ ⊞ 🐟 ➤ ◈ 🆂

S53240-4 Nannacara aureocephalus   MALE
GOLDHEAD - NANNACARA
Fr.-Guayana, W, Male 9cm + Female 5cm

S53240-4 Nannacara aureocephalus   MALE
GOLDHEAD - NANNACARA   BREEDING
Fr.-Guayana, B, Male 9cm + Female 5cm

S53280-4 Nannacara taenia   MALE
TAENIA - NANNACARA
Guayana, W, Male 9cm + Female 5cm

S92009-3 Taeniacara candidi (= Apistogramma weisei) MALE
TORPEDO - CICHLID
Amazonas-Area/Brazil, near Manaus, W, M.7cm+F.5cm

S92009-3 Taeniacara candidi (= Apistogramma weisei) Female
TORPEDO - CICHLID
Amazonas-Area/Brazil, near Manaus, W, M.7cm+F.5cm

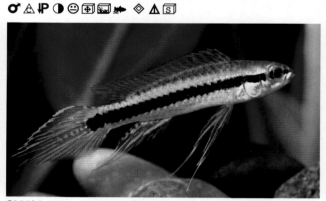

S92010-4 Taeniacara candidi (= Apistogramma weisei) "BLUE"
BLUE-TORPEDO - CICHLID
Amazonas-Area/Brazil, near Manaus, W, M.7cm+F.5cm

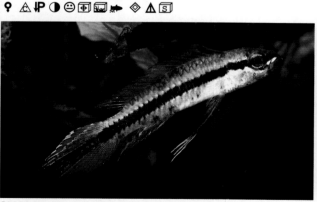

S92011-4 Taeniacara candidi (= Apistogramma weisei) "RED"
RED-TORPEDO - CICHLID   MALE
Amazonas-Area/Brazil, near Manaus, W, M.7cm+F.5cm

S92009-4 Taeniacara candidi (= Apistogramma weisei) PAIR
TORPEDO - CICHLID
Amazonas-Area/Brazil, near Manaus, W, M.7cm+F.5cm

© A.C.S. Glaser GmbH

Lieber Leser,

Sollten Sie im Besitz kleiner oder großer Dia- oder Foto-Sammlungen sein, bitte setzen Sie sich mit uns in Verbindung. Wir suchen für unsere nächsten Bücher immer gute Bilder von allen Fisch-Arten und besonders schönen Aquarien, und würden Ihre Bilder, natürlich gegen eine angemessene Benutzungsgebühr, gerne veröffentlichen.

To our readers,

if you are in possession of either a small or large collection of slides or photographs please contact us. For our upcoming books we are always on the lookout for good pictures of all types of fish and also for attractive aquariums. We would like to publish your photographs - obviously for a suitable charge.

In regelmäßigen Abständen erscheinen Ergänzungen mit neuen Fisch-Bildern, die können Sie

hier

einkleben, damit Sie immer "up-to-date" sind.

Supplements featuring new fish-photographs will be issued on regular basis. Stick them in

here

so that your collection is always up to date.

© A.C.S. Glaser GmbH

In regelmäßigen Abständen erscheinen Ergänzungen
mit neuen Fisch-Bildern, die können Sie

hier

einkleben, damit Sie immer "up-to-date" sind.

Supplements featuring new fish-photographs will be
issued on regular basis. Stick them in

here

so that your collection is always up to date.

In regelmäßigen Abständen erscheinen Ergänzungen mit neuen Fisch-Bildern, die können Sie

hier

einkleben, damit Sie immer "up-to-date" sind.

Supplements featuring new fish-photographs will be issued on regular basis. Stick them in

here

so that your collection is always up to date.

© **A.C.S. Glaser GmbH**

In regelmäßigen Abständen erscheinen Ergänzungen
mit neuen Fisch-Bildern, die können Sie

hier

einkleben, damit Sie immer "up-to-date" sind.

Supplements featuring new fish-photographs will be
issued on regular basis. Stick them in

here

so that your collection is always up to date.

In regelmäßigen Abständen erscheinen Ergänzungen
mit neuen Fisch-Bildern, die können Sie

hier

einkleben, damit Sie immer "up-to-date" sind.

Supplements featuring new fish-photographs will be
issued on regular basis. Stick them in

here

so that your collection is always up to date.

In regelmäßigen Abständen erscheinen Ergänzungen mit neuen Fisch-Bildern, die können Sie

hier

einkleben, damit Sie immer "up-to-date" sind.

Supplements featuring new fish-photographs will be issued on regular basis. Stick them in

here

so that your collection is always up to date.

In regelmäßigen Abständen erscheinen Ergänzungen
mit neuen Fisch-Bildern, die können Sie

hier

einkleben, damit Sie immer "up-to-date" sind.

Supplements featuring new fish-photographs will be
issued on regular basis. Stick them in

here

so that your collection is always up to date.

© **A.C.S. Glaser GmbH**

© A.C.S. Glaser GmbH

ACHTUNG / *ATTENTION*:

Einige Arten jetzt umbenannt:
Some species are now newly named:

all Dicrossus	vorher / *before*	Crenicara
all Microgeophagus	vorher / *before*	Papiliochromis

INDEX
Alphabet

INDEX
Alphabet

INDEX
Alphabet

INDEX
Alphabet

INDEX
Alphabet

INDEX
Alphabet

ACHTUNG / *ATTENTION*:

Einige Arten jetzt umbenannt:
Some species are now newly named:

all Dicrossus	vorher / *before*	Crenicara
all Microgeophagus	vorher / *before*	Papiliochromis

Index der Bildautoren
index of the photographers

Dieter Bork

1xS.22, 1xS.23, 1xS.34, 1xS.44, 1xS.57, 1xS.60, 1xS03330, 1xS03406, 1xS03455, 1xS03530, 1xS03535, 1xS03592, 1xS03627, 1xS03636, 1xS03685, 1xS03715, 1xS03725, 1xS03742, 1xS03800, 1xS03805, 1xS03820, 1xS04250, 1xS04270, 1xS04360, 1xS31160, 2xS03785, 2xS03810,

Jürgen Glaser

1xS.22, 1xS.31, 1xS.35, 1xS.44, 1xS.69, 1xS.74, 1xS03305, 1xS03315, 1xS03320, 1xS03360, 1xS03362, 1xS03372, 1xS03378, 1xS03384, 1xS03416, 1xS03417, 1xS03418, 1xS03420, 1xS03525, 1xS03566, 1xS03590, 1xS03591, 1xS03600, 1xS03605, 1xS03627, 1xS03636, 1xS03740, 1xS03755, 1xS03848, 1xS03890, 1xS03956, 1xS03995, 1xS04015, 1xS52005, 1xS53240, 1xS92011, 2xS.52, 2xS03313, 2xS03383, 2xS03387, 2xS03404, 2xS03466, 2xS03506, 2xS03565, 2xS03588, 2xS03589, 2xS03606, 2xS03625, 2xS03635, 2xS03650, 2xS03652, 2xS03685, 2xS03725, 2xS03816, 2xS03860, 2xS03960, 2xS04250, 2xS04270, 2xS04320, 2xS52020, 2xS52038, 2xS53215, 3xS03459, 3xS31160, 3xS31186, 6xS04500, 7xS52006,

Horst Linke

1xS04045,

Hans J. Mayland

1xS.60, 1xS.69, 1xS.75, 1xS.79, 1xS03310, 1xS03330, 1xS03332, 1xS03334, 1xS03336, 1xS03364, 1xS03372, 1xS03388, 1xS03390, 1xS03391, 1xS03420, 1xS03430, 1xS03465, 1xS03525, 1xS03545, 1xS03569, 1xS03570, 1xS03582, 1xS03656, 1xS03725, 1xS03815, 1xS03848, 1xS03960, 1xS04250, 1xS04430, 1xS07320, 1xS22820, 1xS22820, 1xS31195, 1xS52005, 1xS52013, 1xS52035, 1xS53240, 1xS53280, 1xS92010, 2xS03418, 2xS03838,

Hans J. Mayland/Ulrich Glaser sen.

1xS03368, 1xS03520, 1xS52045, 1xS53205,

Willy Mikschowski

1xS03417,

Jens Pinnhard/Ulrich Glaser sen.

1xS03315, 1xS03327, 1xS03344, 1xS03389, 1xS03406, 1xS03650, 1xS03670, 1xS03742, 1xS03820, 1xS03990, 1xS04005, 1xS04280, 1xS52035, 2xS03366, 2xS03412, 2xS03435, 2xS03905, 2xS04015, 2xS04320, 2xS04450, 2xS22815, 2xS52005, 2xS52020,

Hans Reinhard/Burkhard Migge

1xS03305, 1xS03395,

H.J. Richter

1xS.64, 1xS03327, 1xS03389, 1xS03416, 1xS03430, 1xS03445, 1xS03528, 1xS03560, 1xS03600, 2xS03376,

Uwe Römer

1xS.49, 1xS.80, 1xS03323, 1xS03340, 1xS03430, 1xS03432, 1xS03445, 1xS03465, 1xS03468, 1xS03476, 1xS03480, 1xS03485, 1xS03487, 1xS03490, 1xS03495, 1xS03520, 1xS03522, 1xS03525, 1xS03535, 1xS03545, 1xS03560, 1xS03565, 1xS03581, 1xS03605, 1xS03654, 1xS03685, 1xS03695, 1xS03786, 1xS03805, 1xS03835, 1xS03845, 1xS03857, 1xS03865, 1xS03890, 1xS03915, 1xS03965, 1xS03970, 1xS04010, 1xS04030, 1xS04250, 1xS04270, 1xS04360, 1xS04370, 1xS04380, 1xS53205, 1xS53215, 1xS92009, 2xS.39, 2xS03325, 2xS03385, 2xS03402, 2xS03455, 2xS03475, 2xS03505, 2xS03526, 2xS03538, 2xS03540, 2xS03550, 2xS03584, 2xS03626, 2xS03635, 2xS03698, 2xS03701, 2xS03705, 2xS03725, 2xS03740, 2xS03755, 2xS03770, 2xS03787, 2xS03795, 2xS03817, 2xS03850, 2xS03855, 2xS03862, 2xS03895, 2xS03900, 2xS03955, 2xS04400, 2xS04500, 2xS22820, 2xS53210, 3xS03457, 3xS03870, 3xS04005, 3xS04015, 3xS53212, 4xS52005, 6xS03615,

Erwin Schraml

1xS03320, 1xS03338, 1xS03342, 1xS03360, 1xS03815, 1xS07320, 1xS52015, 1xS52036, 2xS03400, 2xS03650, 2xS04500, 2xS31160, 2xS53215, 2xS92009, 3xS31185, 3xS52020,

Werner Seuß

1xS.40, 1xS03683

Frank Warzel

1xS03344, 1xS03487, 1xS03789, 1xS04273, 1xS04365, 1xS31197, 2xS03793, 2xS03925, 2xS22830, 2xS31196, 2xS31198,

Uwe Werner

1xS03362, 1xS03370, 1xS03386, 1xS03408, 1xS03445, 1xS03580, 1xS03760, 1xS03780, 1xS03785, 1xS31199, 1xS52017, 1xS52025, 1xS52040, 2xS03568, 2xS03665, 2xS03675, 2xS03677, 2xS03935, 2xS03940, 2xS03980, 2xS04290, 2xS04295, 2xS04440, 2xS52021, 3xS03975,

Literaturhinweise
literature tips

Mayland, Hans J. (1995)
Cichliden
Landbuchverlag Hannover

Koslowski, Ingo (1985)
Die Buntbarsche der Neuen Welt
Edition Kernen Essen

Schmettkamp, Werner (1982)
Die Zwergcichliden Südamerikas
Landbuchverlag Hannover

Schaefer, Claus (1994)
Erfolg mit Zwergcichliden
Bede-Verlag Ruhmannsfelden

Deutsche Cichliden Gesellschaft e.V.
DCG-Informationen (Monatszeitschrift)
Festschrift zum 25 jährigen Jubiläum
Cichliden
Deutsche Cichliden-Gesellschaft
Frankfurt 1995

Linke, Horst - Staeck, Wolfgang (1992)
Kleine Buntbarsche/Amerikanische Buntbarsche I
Tetra-Verlag Melle

Richter, Hans Joachim (1987)
Zwerg-Buntbarsche
Neumann-Verlag Leibzig; Radebeul

Vierke, Jörg (1977)
Zwergbuntbarsche
Kosmos-Verlag Stuttgart

Quellenverzeichnis
list of sources

Kulander, Sven O. (1980)
Bonner Zoologische Monographien, Nr. 14
Zoologisches Forschungsinstitut und Museum Alexander Koenig, Bonn

Ufermann, Alfred - Allgayer, Robert - Geerts, Martin (1987)
Katalog der Buntbarsche